Working Papers

Volume I (Chapters 1-14)

to accompany

Accounting Principles

Roger H. Hermanson, Ph.D., CPA
Georgia State University

James Don Edwards, Ph.D., CPA
University of Georgia

R. F. Salmonson, Ph.D., CPA
Michigan State University

1986
Third Edition

Business Publications, Inc.
Plano, Texas

Printed in the United States of America.

ISBN 0-256-03418-4

1 2 3 4 5 6 7 8 9 VK 3 2 1 0 9 8 7 6

Contents

(a)   Moonlight Drive In
Income Statement
For the Month Ended _July 31_, 1987

Revenues:		
Ticket Revenue	31,000	
Concession Revenue	5400	
Total Revenues		36400
Expenses:		
Equipment Rent Expense	5000	
Film Rent Expense	9000	
Advertising Expense	700	
Wage Expense	4200	
Utilities Expense	1700	
Total Expense		20600
Net Income		15800

(b)   Moonlight Drive In
Balance Sheet
July 31st, 1987

Assets			Liabilities and Owner's Equity		
Cash	$ 55800		Liabilities:		
Land	100000		Accounts payable	$ 14000	
Total Assets	155800		Notes payable	20000	
			Total Liabilities	34000	
			Owner's equity:		
			Ron Mott, Capital	121800	
			Total Liabilities and Equity	155800	

Chapter 1   Problem 1-2-A or 1-2-B

(a)

Vince Rossi, COMPANY

Summary of Transactions
Month of March 1987

Trans-action	Explanation	Assets				=	Liabilities		+	Owner's Equity
		Cash	Truck	Cleaning Equip-ment	Office Equip-ment		Accounts Payable	Notes Payable		Vince Rossi, Capital
	Beginning Balances	$ -0-	$ -0-	$ -0-	$ -0-	=	$ -0-	$ -0-	+	$ -0-
1	Owner invested cash	150,000								150,000
2	Borrowed money	75,000						75,000		
		225,000								
3	Purchased equipment for cash	-85,500	18,000	20,000	37,500					
		139,500								
4	Purchased equipment on account				22,500		22,500			
					60,000					
5	Paid an account payable	-22,500					-22,500			
		117,000					0			
	End of month balances	$117,000	$18,000	$20,000	$60,000	=	$ 0	$75,000	+	$150,000
					225,000		225,000			

(b) _____ Vince Rossi _____ COMPANY

Balance Sheet

July ___ 31, 1987

Assets		Liabilities and Owner's Equity	
Cash	$117000 —	Liabilities:	
Truck	18000 —	Notes payable	$75000 —
Cleaning Equipment	30000 —	Owner's equity:	
Office Equipment	60000 —	Vince Rossi, Capital	150000 —
Total Assets	225000 —	Total Liability and Equity	225000 —

4

(a)

Mark Taylor COMPANY
Summary of Transactions
Month of October 1987

Trans-action	Explanation	Assets			=	Liabilities	+	Owner's Equity
		Cash	Accounts Receivable	Equipment		Notes Payable		Mark Taylor Capital
1	Owner Investment	120,000						120,000
2	Borrowed (Money)	16,000 / 136,000				16,000 / 16,000		
3	Purchase Equipment	-100,000 / 36,000		100,000 / 100,000				
4	Service Revenue	7,600 / 43,600						7,600 / 127,600
5	Service Revenue		6,000 / 6,000					6,000 / 133,600
6	Wage Expense	-6,600 / 37,000						-6,600 / 127,000
7	Collected Cash on Account	1,600 / 38,600	-1,600 / 4,400					
	End of Month Balances	$38,600	4,400	$100,000	=	$16,000	+	$127,000
				143,000		143,000		

(b)

Mark Taylor COMPANY

Income Statement

For the Month Ended _October_ 31, 1987

Revenues:		
Service Revenue	$ 13600	—
Expenses:		
Wage Expense	6600	—
Net Income	7000	—

(c)

Mark Taylor COMPANY

Balance Sheet

October 31, 1987

Assets			Liabilities and Owner's Equity		
Cash	$ 38600	—	Liabilities:		
Accounts Receivable	4400	—	Notes Payable	$ 16000	—
Equipment	100000	—	Owner's equity:		
			Mark Taylor, Capital	127000	—
Total Assets	143000	—			
			Total Liabilities and Equity	143000	—

(a)   Thomas   COMPANY
Income Statement
For the Month Ended September 30, 1987

Revenues:			
Service Revenue			$ 12000 —
Expenses:			
Gas and Oil Expense	$	840 —	
Advertising Expense		360 —	
Wages Expense		5760 —	
Rent Expense		720 —	
Misc. Expense		48 —	
Total Expenses			7728 —
Net Income			4272 —

(b)   Thomas   COMPANY
Balance Sheet
September 30, 1987

Assets		Liabilities and Owner's Equity	
Cash	$ 18000 —	Liabilities:	
Accounts receivable	3120 —	Accounts payable	$ 2160 —
Cleaning Equipment	14400 —	Notes payable	9600 —
Office Equipment	3600 —		
Truck	7200 —	Owner's equity:	
		Marcie Thomas	34560 —
Total Assets	46320 —	Total Liabilities and Equity	46320 —

Chapter 1 Problem 1-5-A
(a)

RUSSELL JACOBS COMPANY
Summary of Transactions
Month of April 1987

Trans-action	Explanation	Assets			=	Liabilities	+	Owner's Equity
		Cash	Accounts Receivable	Cleaning Equipment	=	Accounts Payable	+	Russell Jacobs, Capital
	Beginning Balances	$ -0-	$ -0-	$ -0-	=	$ -0-	+	$ -0-
1	Owner invested cash	100,000 / 100,000						100,000 / 100,000
2	Purchased cleaning equipment on account			30,000 / 30,000		30,000 / 30,000		
3	Earned service revenue on account		24,000 / 24,000					24,000 / 124,000
4	Collected cash on account	8,000 / 108,000	-8,000 / 16,000					
5	Paid wages	-6,000 / 102,000						-6,000 / 118,000
6	Paid rent	-4,000 / 98,000						114,000
7	Received bill for advertising					1200 / 31,200		-1200 / 112,800
8	Paid account payable	-30,000				-30,000		
	End of month balances	$68,000	$16,000	$30,000	=	$1,200	+	$112,800
			114,000	114,000		114,000		

9

(a)

EMILY GILMER COMPANY
Summary of Transactions
Month of June 1987

Trans-action	Explanation	Assets			Liabilities		Owner's Equity
		Cash	Office Equipment	Accounts Payable	Notes Payable		Emily Gilmer, Capital
	Beginning balances	$ -0-	$ -0-	$ -0-	$ -0-	+	$ -0-
1	Owner invested cash						
2	Borrowed money						
3	Purchased office equipment for cash						
4	Earned service revenue and received cash						
5	Paid wages						
6	Paid rent						
7	Received bill for gas and oil used						
8	Made a payment on loan payable						
	End of month balances	$	$	$	$	+	$

(b)

<u>Russell Jacobs</u> COMPANY

Income Statement

For the Month Ended <u>April</u> 30, 1987

Revenues:		
Service revenue		$ 24000 —
Expenses:		
Wages	$ 6000 —	
Rent Expense	4000 —	
Advertising	1200 —	
Total Expenses		11200 —
Net Income		12800 —
Net Income		

(c)

<u>Russell Jacobs</u> COMPANY

Balance Sheet

<u>April</u> 30, 1987

Assets		Liabilities and Owner's Equity	
Cash	$ 68000 —	Liabilities:	
Accounts Receivable	16000 —	Accounts payable	$ 1200 —
Cleaning Equipment	30000 —		
		Owner's equity:	
		Russel Jacobs, capital	112800 —
Total Assets	114000 —	Total Liabilities and Equity	114000 —

TWILITE THEATER
Summary of Transactions
Month of August 1987

Date 1987		Assets = Cash	Owner's Equity = Robert Foster, Capital
	Beginning balances	$32,000 =	$32,000
Aug. 2	Paid rent	-8,400	-8,400
15	Owner withdrawal	-800	-800
24	Paid advertising	-3,040	-3,040
27	Paid miscellaneous expense	-1,120	-1,120
31	Paid film rental	-8,000	-8,000
31	Received concession revenues	6,960	6,960
31	Received ticket revenue	18,640	18,640
31	Paid wages	-10,320	-10,320
	End of month balances	$28,880 =	$28,880

(a)

SARA PATTISON COMPANY
Summary of Transactions
Month of May 1987

Date 1987	Explanation	Assets		=	Liabilities	+	Owner's Equity
		Cash	Equip-ment	=	Accounts Payable	+	Sara Pattison, Capital
	Beginning balances	$28,000	$ -0-	=	$ -0-	+	$28,000
May 1	Paid rent						
8	Parking services						
17	Investment by owner						
19	Paid advertising						
30	Purchasing equipment						
31	Paid wages						
	End of month balances	$	$	=	$	+	$

(b)   _Twilite_ _____ COMPANY

Income Statement
For the Month Ended _August_ 31, 1987

Revenues:		
Concession Revenue	9920 —	
Ticket Revenue	18640 —	
		28560 —
Expenses:		
Rent	8400 —	
Advertising	3040 —	
Miscellaneous	1120 —	
Film Rental	8000 —	
Wages	10320 —	
Total Expenses		30880 —
Net Loss		2320 —

(c)   _Twilight_ _____ COMPANY

Balance Sheet
August 31, 1987

Assets		Liabilities and Owner's Equity	
Cash	$ 28880 —	Robert Foster	28880 —

Chapter 1   Problem 1-7-A
(a)

TARA TUCKER COMPANY
Summary of Transactions
Month of May 1987

Trans-action	Explanation	Assets: Cash	Assets: Accounts Receivable	Assets: Land	=	Liabilities: Accounts Payable	+	Owner's Equity: Marianne Mills, Capital
	Beginning balances	$ 28,000	$ 80,000	$300,000	=	$72,000	+	$336,000
1	Additional owner investment	100,000						100,000
		128,000						436,000
2	Collected an account receivable	60,000	-60,000					
		188,000	20,000					
3	Paid an account payable	-52,000				-52,000		
		136,000				20,000		
4	Sold land	100,000		-100,000				
		236,000		200,000				
5	Services rendered		190,000					190,000
			210,000					626,000
6	Wages paid	-110,000						-110,000
		126,000						516,000
7	Owner withdrawal	-12,000						-12,000
	End of month balances	$114,000	$210,000	$200,000	=	$20,000	+	$504,000

524,000 ✓ = 524,000

(a)

JOHN ROEBUCK COMPANY
Summary of Transactions
Month of October 1987

| Date 1987 | Explanation | Assets | | = | Liabilities | + | Owner's Equity |
		Cash	Accounts Receivable		Accounts Payable		John Roebuck, Capital
Sept. 30	Beginning balances	$136,000	$12,000	=	$36,000	+	$112,000
Oct. 1	Paid payable						
2	Paid rent						
7	Cash revenue						
10	Collected receivable						
14	Cash revenue						
15	Receivable revenue						
16	Wages paid						
19	Advertising paid						
21	Cash revenue						
24	Expenses payable						
31	Cash revenue						
31	Wages paid						
31	Receivable revenue						
	End of month balances	$	$	=	$	+	$

(b)   _Tara Tucker_ COMPANY

Income Statement

For the Month Ended _May_ 31, 1987

Revenues:		
Decorating Services		190000 —
Expenses:		
Payroll	110000 —	
Total Expenses		110000 —
Net Profit		80000 —

(c)   _Tara Tucker_ COMPANY

Balance Sheet

May 31, 1987

Assets		Liabilities and Owner's Equity	
Cash	$ 114000 —	Liabilities:	
Accounts Receivable	210000 —	Accounts payable	$ 20000 —
Land	200000 —	Owner's equity	
		Tara Tucker, Capital	504000 —
Total Assets	524000 —	Total Liabilities and Equity	524000 —

(a)

SUNSET DRIVE-IN THEATER
Income Statement
For the Month Ended June 30, 1987

Revenues:

Expenses:

Net Income $

(b)

SUNSET DRIVE-IN THEATER
Balance Sheet
June 30, 1987

Assets		Liabilities and Owner's Equity	
Cash	$	Liabilities:	
			$
		Owner's equity	
		Tom Summers, capital	

(c)

Name _Jeff Marza_

Cash

(1) 60,000—	(4) 20,000—
(22) 1,400—	(7) 600—
	(17) 420—
	(30) 1,200—
	(30) 500—

Delivery Revenue

	(12) 2,500—
	(22) 1,400—

Accounts Receivable

(12) 2,500—	

Accounts Payable

	(26) 75—

Prepaid Rent

(7) 600—	

Salaries Expense

(30) 1,200—	

Truck

(4) 20,000—	

Bill Lavey Capital

	(1) 60,000—

Gas and Oil Expense

(17) 420—	

Bill Lavey, Drawing

(30) 500—	

Utilities Expense

(26) 75—	

DATE (or entry no.)		ACCOUNT TITLES AND EXPLANATION	POST. REF.	DEBIT	CREDIT
Aug	2	Cash		180000 —	
		Dale Jackson, Capital			180000 —
		Owner Investment.			
	3	Rent Expense		3150 —	
		Cash			3150 —
		Building and Equipment Rental for Aug.			
	4	Truck		24000 —	
		Cash			24000 —
		Purchased New Truck.			
	6	Cash		27000 —	
		Sales Revenue			27000 —
		Sales Revenue — cash			
	13	Accounts Receivable		24000 —	
		Sales Revenue			24000 —
		Sales on Account			
	15	Gas and Oil Expense		591 —	
		Cash			591 —
		Gas Bill paid			
	28	Cash		22500 —	
		Accounts Receivable			22500 —
		Received Cash from Account.			
	31	Salary Expense		8100 —	
		Cash			8100 —
		Salaries for August			
	31	Utilities Expense		465 —	
		Accounts Payable			465 —
		August gas and Electric Bill.		289806 —	289806 —
				289806 —	289806 —

Putnam COMPANY

Trial Balance

December 31, 1987

ACCT. NO.	ACCOUNT TITLE	DEBITS	CREDITS
	Cash	7480 —	
	Accounts Receivable	16390 —	
	Prepaid Insurance	1980 —	
	Unearned Delivery Fees	3300 —	3300 —
	Delivery Equipment	35200 —	
	Office Equipment	9900 —	
	Accounts Payable		11000 —
	Notes Payable		16940 —
	Skip Putnam, Capital		31130 —
	Skip Putnam, Drawing	6600 —	
	Delivery Revenue		40700 —
	Rent Expense	3960 —	
	Supplies Expense	1320 —	
	Utilities Expense	2640 —	
	Salaries Expense	17600 —	
		103070 —	103070 —

Name_____

_____

_____ COMPANY

T-Accounts

(a)   Cash   Notes Payable

_____|_____   _____|_____
                 | |
                 | |
                 | |
                 | |

                                                          _____ _____, Capital
                                                          _____|_____
                                                                           |
                                                                           |

_____|_____   _____|_____
                 | |
                 | |

_____|_____   _____|_____
                 | |
                 | |

                                                              Wages Expense
_____|_____   _____|_____
                 | |
                 | |
                 | |

                                                          Gas and Oil Expense
          Accounts Payable   _____|_____
_____|_____ |
                 | |
                 |
                 |
                 |

(b) _____   _____ COMPANY

Trial Balance

_____ ____, 1987

ACCT. NO.	ACCOUNT TITLE	DEBITS	CREDITS
	Cash		

Name_____

(a)

_____ COMPANY
T-Accounts

Cash

(b) _____ COMPANY

Trial Balance

_____ ____, 1987

ACCT. NO.	ACCOUNT TITLE	DEBITS	CREDITS
	Cash		
	Accounts Receivable		

(b)

GENERAL JOURNAL

Page 1

DATE	ACCOUNT TITLES AND EXPLANATION	POST. REF.	DEBIT	CREDIT
1987				

(b) (Concluded)   **GENERAL JOURNAL**   Page 2

DATE	ACCOUNT TITLES AND EXPLANATION	POST. REF.	DEBIT	CREDIT
1987				

(a) and (c)

Cash   ACCOUNT NO.

DATE 1987	EXPLANATION	POST. REF.	DEBIT	CREDIT	BALANCE

Accounts Receivable   ACCOUNT NO.

DATE 1987	EXPLANATION	POST. REF.	DEBIT	CREDIT	BALANCE

Land   ACCOUNT NO.

DATE 1987	EXPLANATION	POST. REF.	DEBIT	CREDIT	BALANCE

Accounts Payable   ACCOUNT NO.

DATE 1987	EXPLANATION	POST. REF.	DEBIT	CREDIT	BALANCE

(a) and (c) (Continued)

ACCOUNT NO.

DATE 1987		EXPLANATION	POST. REF.	DEBIT	CREDIT	BALANCE

ACCOUNT NO.

DATE 1987		EXPLANATION	POST. REF.	DEBIT	CREDIT	BALANCE

ACCOUNT NO.

DATE 1987		EXPLANATION	POST. REF.	DEBIT	CREDIT	BALANCE

ACCOUNT NO.

DATE 1987		EXPLANATION	POST. REF.	DEBIT	CREDIT	BALANCE

ACCOUNT NO.

DATE 1987		EXPLANATION	POST. REF.	DEBIT	CREDIT	BALANCE

ACCOUNT NO.

DATE 1987		EXPLANATION	POST. REF.	DEBIT	CREDIT	BALANCE

(a) and (c) (Continued)

ACCOUNT NO._____

DATE 1987		EXPLANATION	POST. REF.	DEBIT	CREDIT	BALANCE

ACCOUNT NO._____

DATE 1987		EXPLANATION	POST. REF.	DEBIT	CREDIT	BALANCE

ACCOUNT NO._____

DATE 1987		EXPLANATION	POST. REF.	DEBIT	CREDIT	BALANCE

ACCOUNT NO._____

DATE 1987		EXPLANATION	POST. REF.	DEBIT	CREDIT	BALANCE

ACCOUNT NO._____

DATE 1987		EXPLANATION	POST. REF.	DEBIT	CREDIT	BALANCE

ACCOUNT NO._____

DATE 1987		EXPLANATION	POST. REF.	DEBIT	CREDIT	BALANCE

(a) and (c) (Concluded)

ACCOUNT NO.

DATE 1987		EXPLANATION	POST. REF.	DEBIT	CREDIT	BALANCE

ACCOUNT NO.

DATE 1987		EXPLANATION	POST. REF.	DEBIT	CREDIT	BALANCE

(d) _____ COMPANY

Trial Balance

_____ ____, 1987

ACCT. NO.	ACCOUNT TITLE	DEBITS	CREDITS

_____ COMPANY

Trial Balance

December 31, 1987

ACCOUNT TITLE	DEBITS	CREDITS
Cash		
Accounts Receivable		

(a)

GENERAL JOURNAL

DATE	ACCOUNT TITLES AND EXPLANATION	POST. REF.	DEBIT	CREDIT
1987				

(b)

	Cash	

	Service Revenue	

	Advertising Expense	

	Gas and Oil Expense	

	Phillip Gunnels, Capital	

	Miscellaneous Expense	

	Phillip Gunnels, Drawing	

(c)

Billy Reeves COMPANY
GENERAL JOURNAL

DATE	ACCOUNT TITLES AND EXPLANATION	POST. REF.	DEBIT	CREDIT
1987				
Dec. 31				

_____ COMPANY
GENERAL JOURNAL

(a)

DATE	ACCOUNT TITLES AND EXPLANATION	POST. REF.	DEBIT	CREDIT
1987				

(b)   T-Accounts

_____ Depreciation Expense _____   _____ Accumulated Depreciation _____

_____ COMPANY

(a)   **GENERAL JOURNAL**

DATE		ACCOUNT TITLES AND EXPLANATION	POST. REF.	DEBIT	CREDIT
1987		Case 1			
Dec.	31				
		Case 2			
Dec.	31				
		Case 3			
Dec.	31				

(b)

T-Accounts
Case 1

Case 2

Case 3

(c) and (d)

(c)	Case 1									
	Case 2									
	Case 3									
(d)	Case 1									
	Case 2									
	Case 3									

_____ COMPANY
GENERAL JOURNAL   Page ___ (assumed)

(a)

DATE 1987		ACCOUNT TITLES AND EXPLANATION	POST. REF.	DEBIT	CREDIT
Dec.	31				

(b)   **GENERAL LEDGER**

ACCOUNT NO.

DATE 1987		EXPLANATION	POST. REF.	DEBIT	CREDIT	BALANCE

ACCOUNT NO.

DATE 1987		EXPLANATION	POST. REF.	DEBIT	CREDIT	BALANCE

ACCOUNT NO.

DATE 1987		EXPLANATION	POST. REF.	DEBIT	CREDIT	BALANCE

ACCOUNT NO.

DATE 1987		EXPLANATION	POST. REF.	DEBIT	CREDIT	BALANCE

ACCOUNT NO.

DATE 1987		EXPLANATION	POST. REF.	DEBIT	CREDIT	BALANCE

ACCOUNT NO.

DATE 1987		EXPLANATION	POST. REF.	DEBIT	CREDIT	BALANCE

(b) (Concluded)

ACCOUNT NO. _____

DATE 1987	EXPLANATION	POST. REF.	DEBIT	CREDIT	BALANCE

ACCOUNT NO. _____

DATE 1987	EXPLANATION	POST. REF.	DEBIT	CREDIT	BALANCE

_____ COMPANY
GENERAL JOURNAL

(a)

DATE		ACCOUNT TITLES AND EXPLANATION	POST. REF.	DEBIT	CREDIT
1987					
Dec.	31				

(b)

GENERAL LEDGER

Accounts Receivable   ACCOUNT NO.

DATE 1987	EXPLANATION	POST. REF.	DEBIT	CREDIT	BALANCE

ACCOUNT NO.

DATE 1987	EXPLANATION	POST. REF.	DEBIT	CREDIT	BALANCE

ACCOUNT NO.

DATE 1987	EXPLANATION	POST. REF.	DEBIT	CREDIT	BALANCE

ACCOUNT NO.

DATE 1987	EXPLANATION	POST. REF.	DEBIT	CREDIT	BALANCE

ACCOUNT NO.

DATE 1987	EXPLANATION	POST. REF.	DEBIT	CREDIT	BALANCE

(b) (Concluded)

ACCOUNT NO. _____

DATE 1987	EXPLANATION	POST. REF.	DEBIT	CREDIT	BALANCE

ACCOUNT NO. _____

DATE 1987	EXPLANATION	POST. REF.	DEBIT	CREDIT	BALANCE

ACCOUNT NO. _____

DATE 1987	EXPLANATION	POST. REF.	DEBIT	CREDIT	BALANCE

ACCOUNT NO. _____

DATE 1987	EXPLANATION	POST. REF.	DEBIT	CREDIT	BALANCE

ACCOUNT NO. _____

DATE 1987	EXPLANATION	POST. REF.	DEBIT	CREDIT	BALANCE

_____ **COMPANY**

GENERAL JOURNAL

DATE (or entry no.)	ACCOUNT TITLES AND EXPLANATION	POST. REF.	DEBIT	CREDIT
1987				

(a)

(b)

Exhibit A
Book Value of Assets Employed
At December 31, 1987

(b) (Concluded)

Exhibit B

Approximate Income Statement for 1987

Problem 4-1-A or 4-1-B appears in back of manual
Problem 4-2-A or 4-2-B Part (a) appears in back of manual

(b)   **GENERAL JOURNAL**

DATE	ACCOUNT TITLES AND EXPLANATION	POST. REF.	DEBIT	CREDIT

(c)   **GENERAL JOURNAL**

DATE	ACCOUNT TITLES AND EXPLANATION	POST. REF.	DEBIT	CREDIT

(a)

GENERAL JOURNAL

DATE	ACCOUNT TITLES AND EXPLANATION	POST. REF.	DEBIT	CREDIT

(b)

(b) (Concluded)

Income Summary

_____ , Capital

_____ , Drawing

(c)

Income Statement

For the Month Ended December 31, 1987

Revenue:		
Expenses:		
Net Income		

(a)   **GENERAL JOURNAL**

DATE	ACCOUNT TITLES AND EXPLANATION	POST. REF.	DEBIT	CREDIT

(b)

(b) (Concluded)

Problem 4-5-A or 4-5-B Part (a) appears in back of manual

(b) _____ _____

Income Statement

For the Year Ended December 31, 1987

Revenue:

Expenses:

(c) _____ _____

Statement of Owner's Equity

For the Year Ended December 31, 1987

(d)   _____ COMPANY

Balance Sheet

December 31, 1987

	ASSETS												
	Current assets:												
	Property, plant, and equipment:												
	LIABILITIES AND OWNER'S EQUITY												
	Current liabilities:												
	Owner's equity:												

(e)   **GENERAL JOURNAL**

DATE		ACCOUNT TITLES AND EXPLANATION	POST. REF.	DEBIT	CREDIT	
1987		Closing Entries				
Dec.	31					

Problem 4-6-A or 4-6-B Part (a) appears in back of manual.

(b) _____ COMPANY

Income Statement

For the Year Ended December 31, 1987

Revenue:

Expenses:

Net Income

(c)

_____ COMPANY

Statement of Owner's Equity

For the Year Ended December 31, 1987

_____ _____, Capital, January 1, 1987

Net income for 1987

Less: Drawings

_____, Capital, December 31, 1987

(d) _____ COMPANY

Balance Sheet

December 31, 1987

ASSETS							
Current assets:							
Property, plant, and equipment:							
LIABILITIES AND OWNER'S EQUITY							
Current liabilities:							
Owner's equity:							

(e)   **GENERAL JOURNAL**

DATE	ACCOUNT TITLES AND EXPLANATION	POST. REF.	DEBIT	CREDIT
	Adjusting Entries			

(f)

GENERAL JOURNAL

DATE	ACCOUNT TITLES AND EXPLANATION	POST. REF.	DEBIT	CREDIT
	Closing Entries			

Problem 4-7-A or 4-7-B Part (a) appears in back of manual

(b) _____

Income Statement

For the Year Ended December 31, 1987

Revenue(s):

Expenses:

Net Income

(c) _____

Statement of Owner's Equity

For the Year Ended December 31, 1987

_____ , Capital, January 1, 1987

Net Income for 1987

   Total

Less: Drawings

_____ , Capital, December 31, 1987

(d) _____

Balance Sheet
For the Year Ended December 31, 1987

ASSETS											
Current assets:											
Property, plant, and equipment:											
LIABILITIES AND OWNER'S EQUITY											
Current liabilities:											
Owner's equity:											

(e)

GENERAL JOURNAL

DATE	ACCOUNT TITLES AND EXPLANATION	POST. REF.	DEBIT	CREDIT
	Adjusting Entries			

(e) (Continued)   **GENERAL JOURNAL**

DATE	ACCOUNT TITLES AND EXPLANATION	POST. REF.	DEBIT	CREDIT
	Closing Entries			

(f)

Post-Closing Trial Balance

_____ , 1987

SANDY AND ROBBIE BARRON

Income Statement

For the Year Ended December 31, 1987

Revenue				
Expenses				
Net Income				

(a)

EDDIE BROWN

Income Statement

For the Year Ended December 31, 1987

Revenues:										
Expenses:										
Net Income										

EDDIE BROWN

Statement of Owner's Equity

For the Year Ended December 31, 1987

Eddie Brown, Capital, January 1, 1987										
Add: Net Income										
Less: Withdrawals										
Eddie Brown, Capital, December 31, 1987										

(b)

(c)

(d)

MOORE DELIVERY SERVICE COMPANY
GENERAL LEDGER

(a) (b) (d) (g) (h)

Cash   ACCOUNT NO. **100**

DATE 1987	EXPLANATION	POST. REF.	DEBIT	CREDIT	BALANCE

Accounts Receivable   ACCOUNT NO. **101**

DATE 1987	EXPLANATION	POST. REF.	DEBIT	CREDIT	BALANCE

Supplies on Hand   ACCOUNT NO. **102**

DATE 1987	EXPLANATION	POST. REF.	DEBIT	CREDIT	BALANCE

Prepaid Insurance   ACCOUNT NO. **103**

DATE 1987	EXPLANATION	POST. REF.	DEBIT	CREDIT	BALANCE

Prepaid Rent   ACCOUNT NO. **104**

DATE 1987	EXPLANATION	POST. REF.	DEBIT	CREDIT	BALANCE

(a) (b) (d) (g) (h) (Continued)

Building   ACCOUNT NO. 110

DATE 1987		EXPLANATION	POST. REF.	DEBIT	CREDIT	BALANCE

Accumulated Depreciation – Building   ACCOUNT NO. 110A

DATE 1987		EXPLANATION	POST. REF.	DEBIT	CREDIT	BALANCE

Trucks   ACCOUNT NO. 111

DATE 1987		EXPLANATION	POST. REF.	DEBIT	CREDIT	BALANCE

Accumulated Depreciation – Trucks   ACCOUNT NO. 111A

DATE 1987		EXPLANATION	POST. REF.	DEBIT	CREDIT	BALANCE

Accounts Payable   ACCOUNT NO. 200

DATE 1987		EXPLANATION	POST. REF.	DEBIT	CREDIT	BALANCE

Accrued Salaries Payable   ACCOUNT NO. 201

DATE 1987		EXPLANATION	POST. REF.	DEBIT	CREDIT	BALANCE

(a) (b) (d) (g) (h) (Continued)

M. Moore, Capital ACCOUNT NO. 300

DATE 1987	EXPLANATION	POST. REF.	DEBIT	CREDIT	BALANCE

M. Moore, Drawing ACCOUNT NO. 301

DATE 1987	EXPLANATION	POST. REF.	DEBIT	CREDIT	BALANCE

Delivery Service Revenue ACCOUNT NO. 400

DATE 1987	EXPLANATION	POST. REF.	DEBIT	CREDIT	BALANCE

Supplies Expense ACCOUNT NO. 500

DATE 1987	EXPLANATION	POST. REF.	DEBIT	CREDIT	BALANCE

Insurance Expense ACCOUNT NO. 501

DATE 1987	EXPLANATION	POST. REF.	DEBIT	CREDIT	BALANCE

(a) (b) (d) (g) (h) (Continued)

Rent Expense

ACCOUNT NO. **502**

DATE 1987		EXPLANATION	POST. REF.	DEBIT	CREDIT	BALANCE

Depreciation Expense – Building

ACCOUNT NO. **503**

DATE 1987		EXPLANATION	POST. REF.	DEBIT	CREDIT	BALANCE

Depreciation Expense – Trucks

ACCOUNT NO. **504**

DATE 1987		EXPLANATION	POST. REF.	DEBIT	CREDIT	BALANCE

Salaries Expense

ACCOUNT NO. **505**

DATE 1987		EXPLANATION	POST. REF.	DEBIT	CREDIT	BALANCE

Utilities Expense

ACCOUNT NO. **506**

DATE 1987		EXPLANATION	POST. REF.	DEBIT	CREDIT	BALANCE

(a) (b) (d) (g) (h) (Concluded)

Miscellaneous Expense ACCOUNT NO. 507

DATE 1987		EXPLANATION	POST. REF.	DEBIT	CREDIT	BALANCE

Income Summary ACCOUNT NO. 600

DATE 1987		EXPLANATION	POST. REF.	DEBIT	CREDIT	BALANCE

(c)

MOORE DELIVERY SERVICE COMPANY
GENERAL JOURNAL

DATE		ACCOUNT TITLES AND EXPLANATION	POST. REF.	DEBIT	CREDIT

Review Problem 4-1 Part (e) appears in back of manual.

(f)   MOORE DELIVERY SERVICE COMPANY
                                                      Income Statement
                                              For the Month Ended June 30, 1987

Revenue:						
Expenses:						
Net Income						

MOORE DELIVERY SERVICE COMPANY

Statement of Owner's Equity

For the Month Ended June 30, 1987

Beginning capital balance, June 1, 1987						
Add: Net income for June						
Deduct: Withdrawals						
Ending capital balance, June 30						

(f) (Concluded)   **MOORE DELIVERY SERVICE COMPANY**
Balance Sheet
June 30, 1987

ASSETS								
Current Assets:								
Property, Plant, and Equipment:								
LIABILITIES AND OWNER'S EQUITY								
Current Liabilities:								
Owner's Equity:								

MOORE DELIVERY SERVICE CO.
GENERAL JOURNAL

(g)   Page 11

DATE	ACCOUNT TITLES AND EXPLANATION	POST. REF.	DEBIT	CREDIT
	Adjusting Entries			

(h)

MOORE DELIVERY SERVICE CO.
GENERAL JOURNAL

DATE	ACCOUNT TITLES AND EXPLANATION	POST. REF.	DEBIT	CREDIT
	Closing Entries			

(i)

MOORE DELIVERY SERVICE COMPANY
Post-Closing Trial Balance
June 30, 1987

ACCT. NO.	ACCOUNT TITLE	DEBITS	CREDITS

(a)

_____ COMPANY
GENERAL JOURNAL

DATE	ACCOUNT TITLES AND EXPLANATION	POST. REF.	DEBIT	CREDIT

(b)

_____ COMPANY

GENERAL JOURNAL

DATE	ACCOUNT TITLES AND EXPLANATION	POST. REF.	DEBIT	CREDIT

_____ **COMPANY**
GENERAL JOURNAL

DATE	ACCOUNT TITLES AND EXPLANATION	POST. REF.	DEBIT	CREDIT

_____ **COMPANY**
GENERAL JOURNAL

DATE	ACCOUNT TITLES AND EXPLANATION	POST. REF.	DEBIT	CREDIT

GENERAL JOURNAL

DATE	ACCOUNT TITLES AND EXPLANATION	POST. REF.	DEBIT	CREDIT

_____ **COMPANY**

(a)   **GENERAL JOURNAL**

DATE		ACCOUNT TITLES AND EXPLANATION	POST. REF.	DEBIT	CREDIT
1987					
June	1				

(a) (Concluded)   **GENERAL JOURNAL**

DATE	ACCOUNT TITLES AND EXPLANATION	POST. REF.	DEBIT	CREDIT

GENERAL LEDGER

(b)

Cash   ACCOUNT NO.

DATE 1987	EXPLANATION	POST. REF.	DEBIT	CREDIT	BALANCE

Accounts Receivable   ACCOUNT NO.

DATE 1987	EXPLANATION	POST. REF.	DEBIT	CREDIT	BALANCE

Merchandise Inventory   ACCOUNT NO.

DATE 1987	EXPLANATION	POST. REF.	DEBIT	CREDIT	BALANCE

Accounts Payable   ACCOUNT NO.

DATE 1987	EXPLANATION	POST. REF.	DEBIT	CREDIT	BALANCE

(b) (Continued)

Paul Maddox, Capital   ACCOUNT NO.

DATE 1987		EXPLANATION	POST. REF.	DEBIT	CREDIT	BALANCE

Sales   ACCOUNT NO.

DATE 1987		EXPLANATION	POST. REF.	DEBIT	CREDIT	BALANCE

Sales Discounts   ACCOUNT NO.

DATE 1987		EXPLANATION	POST. REF.	DEBIT	CREDIT	BALANCE

Sales Returns and Allowances   ACCOUNT NO.

DATE 1987		EXPLANATION	POST. REF.	DEBIT	CREDIT	BALANCE

Purchases   ACCOUNT NO.

DATE 1987		EXPLANATION	POST. REF.	DEBIT	CREDIT	BALANCE

Purchase Discounts   ACCOUNT NO.

DATE 1987		EXPLANATION	POST. REF.	DEBIT	CREDIT	BALANCE

(b) (Concluded)

Purchase Returns and Allowances   ACCOUNT NO.

DATE 1987		EXPLANATION	POST. REF.	DEBIT	CREDIT	BALANCE

Transportation-In   ACCOUNT NO.

DATE 1987		EXPLANATION	POST. REF.	DEBIT	CREDIT	BALANCE

Delivery Expense   ACCOUNT NO.

DATE 1987		EXPLANATION	POST. REF.	DEBIT	CREDIT	BALANCE

Rent Expense   ACCOUNT NO.

DATE 1987		EXPLANATION	POST. REF.	DEBIT	CREDIT	BALANCE

Sales Salaries Expense   ACCOUNT NO.

DATE 1987		EXPLANATION	POST. REF.	DEBIT	CREDIT	BALANCE

(b)   **GENERAL LEDGER**

Cash   ACCOUNT NO.

DATE 1987		EXPLANATION	POST. REF.	DEBIT	CREDIT	BALANCE

Accounts Receivable   ACCOUNT NO.

DATE 1987		EXPLANATION	POST. REF.	DEBIT	CREDIT	BALANCE

Merchandise Inventory   ACCOUNT NO.

DATE 1987		EXPLANATION	POST. REF.	DEBIT	CREDIT	BALANCE

Land   ACCOUNT NO.

DATE 1987		EXPLANATION	POST. REF.	DEBIT	CREDIT	BALANCE

(b) (Continued)   **GENERAL LEDGER**

Accounts Payable   ACCOUNT NO. _____

DATE 1987	EXPLANATION	POST. REF.	DEBIT	CREDIT	BALANCE

Sam Tate, Capital   ACCOUNT NO. _____

DATE 1987	EXPLANATION	POST. REF.	DEBIT	CREDIT	BALANCE

Sales   ACCOUNT NO. _____

DATE 1987	EXPLANATION	POST. REF.	DEBIT	CREDIT	BALANCE

Sales Discounts   ACCOUNT NO. _____

DATE 1987	EXPLANATION	POST. REF.	DEBIT	CREDIT	BALANCE

Sales Returns and Allowances   ACCOUNT NO. _____

DATE 1987	EXPLANATION	POST. REF.	DEBIT	CREDIT	BALANCE

Purchases   ACCOUNT NO. _____

DATE 1987	EXPLANATION	POST. REF.	DEBIT	CREDIT	BALANCE

(b) (Concluded)   **GENERAL LEDGER**

Transportation-In   ACCOUNT NO.

DATE 1987		EXPLANATION	POST. REF.	DEBIT	CREDIT	BALANCE

Purchase Discounts   ACCOUNT NO.

DATE 1987		EXPLANATION	POST. REF.	DEBIT	CREDIT	BALANCE

Purchase Returns and Allowances   ACCOUNT NO.

DATE 1987		EXPLANATION	POST. REF.	DEBIT	CREDIT	BALANCE

Rent Expense   ACCOUNT NO.

DATE 1987		EXPLANATION	POST. REF.	DEBIT	CREDIT	BALANCE

Office Salaries Expense   ACCOUNT NO.

DATE 1987		EXPLANATION	POST. REF.	DEBIT	CREDIT	BALANCE

Sales Salaries Expense   ACCOUNT NO.

DATE 1987		EXPLANATION	POST. REF.	DEBIT	CREDIT	BALANCE

(c) _____ COMPANY

Trial Balance

June 30, 1987

ACCOUNT TITLE	DEBITS	CREDITS

(d) _____ COMPANY

Income Statement

For the Month Ended June 30, 1987

Operating revenues:					
Sales					
Less: Sales discounts					
Sales returns and allowances					
Net Sales					
Cost of goods sold:					
Operating expenses:					
Net Income					

Problem 5-5-A or 5-5-B Part (a) appears in back of manual.

(b) _____ _____ COMPANY

Income Statement

For the Year Ended December 31, 1987

Operating revenues:					
Cost of goods sold:					
Operating expenses:					
Nonoperating revenues and expenses:					

(c) _____ _____ COMPANY

Balance Sheet

December 31, 1987

ASSETS

Current assets:

Property, plant, and equipment:

LIABILITIES AND OWNER'S EQUITY

Current liabilities:

Owner's equity:

_____ COMPANY

(d)

GENERAL JOURNAL

DATE		ACCOUNT TITLES AND EXPLANATION	POST. REF.	DEBIT	CREDIT
1987		Closing Entries			
Dec.	31	Merchandising Inventory			
		Sales			

Name_____

CONNER CABINET COMPANY
GENERAL JOURNAL

(a) and (e)

DATE		ACCOUNT TITLES AND EXPLANATION	POST. REF.	DEBIT	CREDIT
1987					
May	1				

(a) and (f) (Continued)   **GENERAL JOURNAL**

DATE		ACCOUNT TITLES AND EXPLANATION	POST. REF.	DEBIT	CREDIT
(e) or (f)		Closing Entries			
1987					
May	31				

(a) (Concluded) and (e) (Continued)   **GENERAL JOURNAL**

DATE	ACCOUNT TITLES AND EXPLANATION	POST. REF.	DEBIT	CREDIT

(b) and (e)

Cash   ACCOUNT NO.

DATE 1987		EXPLANATION	POST. REF.	DEBIT	CREDIT	BALANCE

Accounts Receivable   ACCOUNT NO.

DATE 1987		EXPLANATION	POST. REF.	DEBIT	CREDIT	BALANCE

Merchandise Inventory   ACCOUNT NO.

DATE 1987		EXPLANATION	POST. REF.	DEBIT	CREDIT	BALANCE

Accounts Payable   ACCOUNT NO.

DATE 1987		EXPLANATION	POST. REF.	DEBIT	CREDIT	BALANCE

(b) and (e) (Continued)

Ron Connors, Capital   ACCOUNT NO.

DATE 1987	EXPLANATION	POST. REF.	DEBIT	CREDIT	BALANCE

Sales   ACCOUNT NO.

DATE 1987	EXPLANATION	POST. REF.	DEBIT	CREDIT	BALANCE

Sales Discounts   ACCOUNT NO.

DATE 1987	EXPLANATION	POST. REF.	DEBIT	CREDIT	BALANCE

Sales Returns and Allowances   ACCOUNT NO.

DATE 1987	EXPLANATION	POST. REF.	DEBIT	CREDIT	BALANCE

Purchases   ACCOUNT NO.

DATE 1987	EXPLANATION	POST. REF.	DEBIT	CREDIT	BALANCE

Purchase Discounts   ACCOUNT NO.

DATE 1987	EXPLANATION	POST. REF.	DEBIT	CREDIT	BALANCE

(b) and (e) (Concluded)

Purchase Returns and Allowances   ACCOUNT NO.

DATE 1987		EXPLANATION	POST. REF.	DEBIT	CREDIT	BALANCE

Transportation-In   ACCOUNT NO.

DATE 1987		EXPLANATION	POST. REF.	DEBIT	CREDIT	BALANCE

Miscellaneous Selling Expenses   ACCOUNT NO.

DATE 1987		EXPLANATION	POST. REF.	DEBIT	CREDIT	BALANCE

Miscellaneous Administrative Expenses   ACCOUNT NO.

DATE 1987		EXPLANATION	POST. REF.	DEBIT	CREDIT	BALANCE

Income Summary   ACCOUNT NO.

DATE 1987		EXPLANATION	POST. REF.	DEBIT	CREDIT	BALANCE

Problem 5-6-A Part (c) continues in back of manual

(d)   **CONNORS CABINET COMPANY**

Income Statement

For the Month Ended May 31, 1987

Operating revenues:

Cost of goods sold:

Operating expenses:

HALL WESTERN WEAR COMPANY
GENERAL JOURNAL

(a) and (f)

DATE		ACCOUNT TITLES AND EXPLANATION	POST. REF.	DEBIT	CREDIT
1987					
May	1				

(a) and (f) (Continued)   **GENERAL JOURNAL**

DATE		ACCOUNT TITLES AND EXPLANATION	POST. REF.	DEBIT	CREDIT
(f)		Closing Entries			
1987					
May	31				

(a) (Concluded) and (f) (Continued)   **GENERAL JOURNAL**

DATE	ACCOUNT TITLES AND EXPLANATION	POST. REF.	DEBIT	CREDIT

HALL WESTERN WEAR COMPANY
GENERAL LEDGER

(b) and (f) (Continued)

Cash   ACCOUNT NO.

DATE 1987		EXPLANATION	POST. REF.	DEBIT	CREDIT	BALANCE

Accounts Receivable   ACCOUNT NO.

DATE 1987		EXPLANATION	POST. REF.	DEBIT	CREDIT	BALANCE

Merchandise Inventory   ACCOUNT NO.

DATE 1987		EXPLANATION	POST. REF.	DEBIT	CREDIT	BALANCE

Land   ACCOUNT NO.

DATE 1987		EXPLANATION	POST. REF.	DEBIT	CREDIT	BALANCE

(b) and (f) (Continued)

Accounts Payable   ACCOUNT NO.

DATE 1987		EXPLANATION	POST. REF.	DEBIT	CREDIT	BALANCE

Mark Hall, Capital   ACCOUNT NO.

DATE 1987		EXPLANATION	POST. REF.	DEBIT	CREDIT	BALANCE

Sales   ACCOUNT NO.

DATE 1987		EXPLANATION	POST. REF.	DEBIT	CREDIT	BALANCE

Sales Discounts   ACCOUNT NO.

DATE 1987		EXPLANATION	POST. REF.	DEBIT	CREDIT	BALANCE

Sales Returns and Allowances   ACCOUNT NO.

DATE 1987		EXPLANATION	POST. REF.	DEBIT	CREDIT	BALANCE

Purchases   ACCOUNT NO.

DATE 1987		EXPLANATION	POST. REF.	DEBIT	CREDIT	BALANCE

(b) and (f) (Continued)

Purchase Discounts   ACCOUNT NO.

DATE 1987		EXPLANATION	POST. REF.	DEBIT	CREDIT	BALANCE

Purchase Returns and Allowances   ACCOUNT NO.

DATE 1987		EXPLANATION	POST. REF.	DEBIT	CREDIT	BALANCE

Transportation-In   ACCOUNT NO.

DATE 1987		EXPLANATION	POST. REF.	DEBIT	CREDIT	BALANCE

Rent Expense   ACCOUNT NO.

DATE 1987		EXPLANATION	POST. REF.	DEBIT	CREDIT	BALANCE

Office Salaries Expense   ACCOUNT NO.

DATE 1987		EXPLANATION	POST. REF.	DEBIT	CREDIT	BALANCE

Sales Salaries Expense   ACCOUNT NO.

DATE 1987		EXPLANATION	POST. REF.	DEBIT	CREDIT	BALANCE

(b) and (f) (Concluded)

	Income Summary			ACCOUNT NO.

DATE 1987		EXPLANATION	POST. REF.	DEBIT	CREDIT	BALANCE

Problem 5-6-B Part (c) continues in back of manual.

(d) _____   **HALL WESTERN WEAR COMPANY**

Income Statement

For the Month Ended May 31, 1987

Operating revenues:

Cost of goods sold:

Operating expenses:

Net Income

(e)
HALL WESTERN WEAR COMPANY
Balance Sheet

May 31, 1987

ASSETS

Current assets:

Property, plant, and equipment:

LIABILITIES AND OWNER'S EQUITY

Owner's equity:

(a)

STEELE'S HARDWARE STORE

Income Statement

For the Six Months Ended June 30, 1987

Operating revenues:

Cost of goods sold:

Operating expenses:

(b)

STEELE'S HARDWARE STORE
Balance Sheet
June 30, 1987

ASSETS

Current assets:

Property, plant and equipment:

LIABILITIES AND OWNER'S EQUITY

Liabilities:

Owner's equity:

Name_____

_____

(a)

SALES JOURNAL

Page _____

DATE		CUSTOMER	INVOICE NUMBER	ACCOUNTS RECEIVABLE, DR. SALES, CR. AMOUNT	✓	

GENERAL LEDGER

Accounts Receivable Control

Sales

SUBSIDIARY ACCOUNTS RECEIVABLE LEDGER

(b)

PURCHASES JOURNAL

Page _____

DATE		CREDITOR	TERMS	INVOICE NUMBER	PURCHASES, DR. ACCOUNTS PAYABLE, CR.	
					AMOUNT	✓

GENERAL LEDGER

Accounts Payable Control

Purchases

SUBSIDIARY ACCOUNTS
PAYABLE LEDGER

(a)

SALES JOURNAL

DATE	CUSTOMER	INVOICE NUMBER	ACCOUNTS RECEIVABLE, DR. SALES, CR. ✓	AMOUNT

CASH RECEIPTS JOURNAL

DATE	DESCRIPTION	SALES, CR.	ACCOUNTS RECEIVABLE, CR. AMOUNT	✓	OTHER ACCOUNTS, CR. ACCOUNT TITLE	ACCT. NO.	AMOUNT	✓	SALES DISCOUNTS, DR.	CASH, DR.

(a) (Concluded)

GENERAL JOURNAL

DATE	ACCOUNT TITLES AND EXPLANATION	POST. REF.	DEBIT	CREDIT
1987				
	Sales Returns and Allowances			

(b)

PARTIAL GENERAL LEDGER

Accounts Receivable   ACCOUNT NO. _____

DATE 1987	EXPLANATION	POST. REF.	DEBIT	CREDIT	BALANCE
	Balance				

SUBSIDIARY ACCOUNTS RECEIVABLE LEDGER

ACCOUNT NO. _____

DATE 1987	EXPLANATION	POST. REF.	DEBIT	CREDIT	BALANCE
	Balance				

ACCOUNT NO. _____

DATE 1987	EXPLANATION	POST. REF.	DEBIT	CREDIT	BALANCE

(b) (Concluded)

ACCOUNT NO.

DATE 1987		EXPLANATION	POST. REF.	DEBIT	CREDIT	BALANCE

ACCOUNT NO.

DATE 1987		EXPLANATION	POST. REF.	DEBIT	CREDIT	BALANCE

ACCOUNT NO.

DATE 1987		EXPLANATION	POST. REF.	DEBIT	CREDIT	BALANCE

ACCOUNT NO.

DATE 1987		EXPLANATION	POST. REF.	DEBIT	CREDIT	BALANCE

(c)

Schedule of Accounts Receivable
As of _____ ____, 1987

Problem 6-3-A or 6-3-B

Name

PURCHASES JOURNAL

(a)

DATE	CREDITOR	TERMS	INVOICE NUMBER	PURCHASES, DR. ACCOUNTS PAYABLE, CR.	
				✓	AMOUNT

CASH DISBURSEMENTS JOURNAL

DATE	DESCRIPTION	CHECK NO.	CASH, CR.	PURCHASE DISCOUNTS, CR.

ACCOUNTS PAYABLE, DR.		OTHER ACCOUNTS, DR.	
AMOUNT	✓	ACCOUNT TITLE	ACCT. NO.	AMOUNT

(a) (Concluded)

GENERAL JOURNAL

DATE		ACCOUNT TITLES AND EXPLANATION	POST. REF.	DEBIT	CREDIT

(b)

PARTIAL GENERAL LEDGER

Accounts Payable   ACCOUNT NO.

DATE 1987		EXPLANATION	POST. REF.	DEBIT	CREDIT	BALANCE

SUBSIDIARY ACCOUNTS PAYABLE LEDGER

DATE 1987		EXPLANATION	POST. REF.	DEBIT	CREDIT	BALANCE

(b) (Continued)

DATE 1987	EXPLANATION	POST. REF.	DEBIT	CREDIT	BALANCE

DATE 1987	EXPLANATION	POST. REF.	DEBIT	CREDIT	BALANCE

DATE 1987	EXPLANATION	POST. REF.	DEBIT	CREDIT	BALANCE

DATE 1987	EXPLANATION	POST. REF.	DEBIT	CREDIT	BALANCE

DATE 1987	EXPLANATION	POST. REF.	DEBIT	CREDIT	BALANCE

(b) (Concluded)

DATE 1987		EXPLANATION	POST. REF.	DEBIT	CREDIT	BALANCE

DATE 1987		EXPLANATION	POST. REF.	DEBIT	CREDIT	BALANCE

(c)

Schedule of Accounts Payable

As of _____ _____, 1987

_____

GENERAL LEDGER

Cash   ACCOUNT NO.

DATE 1987		EXPLANATION	POST. REF.	DEBIT	CREDIT	BALANCE

Accounts Receivable   ACCOUNT NO.

DATE 1987		EXPLANATION	POST. REF.	DEBIT	CREDIT	BALANCE

ACCOUNT NO.

DATE 1987		EXPLANATION	POST. REF.	DEBIT	CREDIT	BALANCE

ACCOUNT NO.

DATE 1987		EXPLANATION	POST. REF.	DEBIT	CREDIT	BALANCE

ACCOUNT NO.

DATE 1987		EXPLANATION	POST. REF.	DEBIT	CREDIT	BALANCE

ACCOUNT NO.

DATE 1987		EXPLANATION	POST. REF.	DEBIT	CREDIT	BALANCE

ACCOUNT NO.

DATE 1987	EXPLANATION	POST. REF.	DEBIT	CREDIT	BALANCE

ACCOUNT NO.

DATE 1987	EXPLANATION	POST. REF.	DEBIT	CREDIT	BALANCE

ACCOUNT NO.

DATE 1987	EXPLANATION	POST. REF.	DEBIT	CREDIT	BALANCE

ACCOUNT NO.

DATE 1987	EXPLANATION	POST. REF.	DEBIT	CREDIT	BALANCE

ACCOUNT NO.

DATE 1987	EXPLANATION	POST. REF.	DEBIT	CREDIT	BALANCE

ACCOUNT NO.

DATE 1987	EXPLANATION	POST. REF.	DEBIT	CREDIT	BALANCE

ACCOUNT NO.

DATE 1987		EXPLANATION	POST. REF.	DEBIT	CREDIT	BALANCE

ACCOUNT NO.

DATE 1987		EXPLANATION	POST. REF.	DEBIT	CREDIT	BALANCE

ACCOUNT NO.

DATE 1987		EXPLANATION	POST. REF.	DEBIT	CREDIT	BALANCE

ACCOUNT NO.

DATE 1987		EXPLANATION	POST. REF.	DEBIT	CREDIT	BALANCE

ACCOUNT NO.

DATE 1987		EXPLANATION	POST. REF.	DEBIT	CREDIT	BALANCE

ACCOUNT NO.

DATE 1987	EXPLANATION	POST. REF.	DEBIT	CREDIT	BALANCE

ACCOUNT NO.

DATE 1987	EXPLANATION	POST. REF.	DEBIT	CREDIT	BALANCE

ACCOUNT NO.

DATE 1987	EXPLANATION	POST. REF.	DEBIT	CREDIT	BALANCE

ACCOUNT NO.

DATE 1987	EXPLANATION	POST. REF.	DEBIT	CREDIT	BALANCE

ACCOUNT NO.

DATE 1987	EXPLANATION	POST. REF.	DEBIT	CREDIT	BALANCE

ACCOUNT NO.

DATE 1987	EXPLANATION	POST. REF.	DEBIT	CREDIT	BALANCE

ACCOUNT NO.

DATE 1987	EXPLANATION	POST. REF.	DEBIT	CREDIT	BALANCE

ACCOUNT NO.

DATE 1987	EXPLANATION	POST. REF.	DEBIT	CREDIT	BALANCE

ACCOUNT NO.

DATE 1987	EXPLANATION	POST. REF.	DEBIT	CREDIT	BALANCE

ACCOUNT NO.

DATE 1987	EXPLANATION	POST. REF.	DEBIT	CREDIT	BALANCE

ACCOUNT NO.

DATE 1987	EXPLANATION	POST. REF.	DEBIT	CREDIT	BALANCE

ACCOUNT NO.

DATE 1987	EXPLANATION	POST. REF.	DEBIT	CREDIT	BALANCE

ACCOUNT NO.

DATE 1987		EXPLANATION	POST. REF.	DEBIT	CREDIT	BALANCE

ACCOUNT NO.

DATE 1987		EXPLANATION	POST. REF.	DEBIT	CREDIT	BALANCE

ACCOUNT NO.

DATE 1987		EXPLANATION	POST. REF.	DEBIT	CREDIT	BALANCE

ACCOUNT NO.

DATE 1987		EXPLANATION	POST. REF.	DEBIT	CREDIT	BALANCE

ACCOUNT NO.

DATE 1987		EXPLANATION	POST. REF.	DEBIT	CREDIT	BALANCE

ACCOUNT NO.

DATE 1987		EXPLANATION	POST. REF.	DEBIT	CREDIT	BALANCE

ACCOUNT NO.

DATE 1987		EXPLANATION	POST. REF.	DEBIT	CREDIT	BALANCE

ACCOUNT NO.

DATE 1987		EXPLANATION	POST. REF.	DEBIT	CREDIT	BALANCE

ACCOUNT NO.

DATE 1987		EXPLANATION	POST. REF.	DEBIT	CREDIT	BALANCE

ACCOUNT NO.

DATE 1987		EXPLANATION	POST. REF.	DEBIT	CREDIT	BALANCE

Trial Balance
December 31, 1987

	DEBITS	CREDITS

Problem 6-5-A or 6-5-B

Name

(a)

SALES JOURNAL

DATE	CUSTOMER	INVOICE NUMBER	ACCOUNTS RECEIVABLE, DR. SALES, CR.	
			AMOUNT	✓

CASH RECEIPTS JOURNAL

CASH, DR.	SALES DISCOUNTS, DR.	DATE	DESCRIPTION	SALES, CR.	ACCOUNTS RECEIVABLE, CR.		OTHER ACCOUNTS, DR.			
					AMOUNT	✓	ACCOUNT TITLE	ACCT. NO.	AMOUNT	✓

Problem 6-5-A or 6-5-B (Continued)

Name

(a) (Continued)

PURCHASES JOURNAL

Page

DATE	CREDITOR	TERMS	INVOICE NUMBER	PURCHASES, DR. ACCOUNTS PAYABLE, CR. AMOUNT	✓

CASH DISBURSEMENTS JOURNAL

Page

DATE	DESCRIPTION	CHECK NO.	CASH, CR.	PURCHASE DISCOUNTS, CR.

ACCOUNTS PAYABLE, DR. AMOUNT	✓	ACCOUNT TITLE	OTHER ACCOUNTS, DR. ACCT. NO.	AMOUNT	✓

(a) (Concluded)

GENERAL JOURNAL

Page ____

DATE	ACCOUNT TITLES AND EXPLANATION	POST. REF.	DEBIT	CREDIT

(b)

GENERAL LEDGER

Cash   ACCOUNT NO. **1**

DATE 1987	EXPLANATION	POST. REF.	DEBIT	CREDIT	BALANCE
	Beginning Balance				

Accounts Receivable   ACCOUNT NO. **2**

DATE 1987	EXPLANATION	POST. REF.	DEBIT	CREDIT	BALANCE

ACCOUNT NO. **3**

DATE 1987	EXPLANATION	POST. REF.	DEBIT	CREDIT	BALANCE

ACCOUNT NO. **4**

DATE 1987	EXPLANATION	POST. REF.	DEBIT	CREDIT	BALANCE

(b) (Continued)

ACCOUNT NO. **5**

DATE 1987		EXPLANATION	POST. REF.	DEBIT	CREDIT	BALANCE

ACCOUNT NO. **6**

DATE 1987		EXPLANATION	POST. REF.	DEBIT	CREDIT	BALANCE

ACCOUNT NO. **7**

DATE 1987		EXPLANATION	POST. REF.	DEBIT	CREDIT	BALANCE

ACCOUNT NO. **8**

DATE 1987		EXPLANATION	POST. REF.	DEBIT	CREDIT	BALANCE

ACCOUNT NO. **9**

DATE 1987		EXPLANATION	POST. REF.	DEBIT	CREDIT	BALANCE

ACCOUNT NO. **10**

DATE 1987		EXPLANATION	POST. REF.	DEBIT	CREDIT	BALANCE

(b) (Concluded)

ACCOUNT NO. **11**

DATE 1987		EXPLANATION	POST. REF.	DEBIT	CREDIT	BALANCE

ACCOUNT NO. **12**

DATE 1987		EXPLANATION	POST. REF.	DEBIT	CREDIT	BALANCE

ACCOUNT NO. **13**

DATE 1987		EXPLANATION	POST. REF.	DEBIT	CREDIT	BALANCE

ACCOUNT NO. **14**

DATE 1987		EXPLANATION	POST. REF.	DEBIT	CREDIT	BALANCE

(c)

_____

Trial Balance

_____ 31, 1987

Cash		
Accounts Receivable		

Chapter 6   Business Decision Problem 6-1

(a)

(b)

Chapter 6   Business Decision Problem 6-1 (Continued)

(b) (Concluded)

(c)

Name

(a)

(b)

Chapter 6   Business Decision Problem 6-2 (Concluded)

(b) (Concluded)

(c)

SPORTSWEAR OUTLET STORE
GENERAL LEDGER

(a) (c) (g)

Cash   ACCOUNT NO.   1

DATE 1987	EXPLANATION	POST. REF.	DEBIT	CREDIT	BALANCE

Accounts Receivable   ACCOUNT NO.   2

DATE 1987	EXPLANATION	POST. REF.	DEBIT	CREDIT	BALANCE

Prepaid Insurance   ACCOUNT NO.   3

DATE 1987	EXPLANATION	POST. REF.	DEBIT	CREDIT	BALANCE

Supplies on Hand   ACCOUNT NO.   4

DATE 1987	EXPLANATION	POST. REF.	DEBIT	CREDIT	BALANCE

Merchandise Inventory   ACCOUNT NO.   5

DATE 1987	EXPLANATION	POST. REF.	DEBIT	CREDIT	BALANCE

(a) (c) (g) (Continued)

Office Furniture   ACCOUNT NO. 6

DATE 1987		EXPLANATION	POST. REF.	DEBIT	CREDIT	BALANCE

Accumulated Depreciation – Office Furniture   ACCOUNT NO. 7

DATE 1987		EXPLANATION	POST. REF.	DEBIT	CREDIT	BALANCE

Store Equipment   ACCOUNT NO. 8

DATE 1987		EXPLANATION	POST. REF.	DEBIT	CREDIT	BALANCE

Accumulated Depreciation – Store Equipment   ACCOUNT NO. 9

DATE 1987		EXPLANATION	POST. REF.	DEBIT	CREDIT	BALANCE

Accounts Payable   ACCOUNT NO. 10

DATE 1987		EXPLANATION	POST. REF.	DEBIT	CREDIT	BALANCE

Jack Springs, Capital   ACCOUNT NO. 11

DATE 1987		EXPLANATION	POST. REF.	DEBIT	CREDIT	BALANCE

(a) (c) (g) (Continued)

Jack Springs, Drawing   ACCOUNT NO. 12

DATE 1987		EXPLANATION	POST. REF.	DEBIT	CREDIT	BALANCE

Sales   ACCOUNT NO. 13

DATE 1987		EXPLANATION	POST. REF.	DEBIT	CREDIT	BALANCE

Sales Discounts   ACCOUNT NO. 14

DATE 1987		EXPLANATION	POST. REF.	DEBIT	CREDIT	BALANCE

Sales Returns and Allowances   ACCOUNT NO. 15

DATE 1987		EXPLANATION	POST. REF.	DEBIT	CREDIT	BALANCE

Miscellaneous Revenue   ACCOUNT NO. 16

DATE 1987		EXPLANATION	POST. REF.	DEBIT	CREDIT	BALANCE

Purchases   ACCOUNT NO. 17

DATE 1987		EXPLANATION	POST. REF.	DEBIT	CREDIT	BALANCE

(a) (c) (g) (Continued)

Purchase Discounts

ACCOUNT NO. **18**

DATE 1987		EXPLANATION	POST. REF.	DEBIT	CREDIT	BALANCE

Purchase Returns and Allowances

ACCOUNT NO. **19**

DATE 1987		EXPLANATION	POST. REF.	DEBIT	CREDIT	BALANCE

Transportation-In

ACCOUNT NO. **20**

DATE 1987		EXPLANATION	POST. REF.	DEBIT	CREDIT	BALANCE

Rent Expense

ACCOUNT NO. **21**

DATE 1987		EXPLANATION	POST. REF.	DEBIT	CREDIT	BALANCE

Insurance Expense

ACCOUNT NO. **22**

DATE 1987		EXPLANATION	POST. REF.	DEBIT	CREDIT	BALANCE

Supplies Expense

ACCOUNT NO. **23**

DATE 1987		EXPLANATION	POST. REF.	DEBIT	CREDIT	BALANCE

(a) (c) (g) (Concluded)

Depreciation Expense – Office Equipment   ACCOUNT NO. 24

DATE 1987	EXPLANATION	POST. REF.	DEBIT	CREDIT	BALANCE

Depreciation Expense – Store Equipment   ACCOUNT NO. 25

DATE 1987	EXPLANATION	POST. REF.	DEBIT	CREDIT	BALANCE

Income Summary   ACCOUNT NO. 26

DATE 1987	EXPLANATION	POST. REF.	DEBIT	CREDIT	BALANCE

(a) (c)

SPORTSWEAR OUTLET STORE
SUBSIDIARY ACCOUNTS RECEIVABLE LEDGER

Sallie Branscom   ACCOUNT NO.

DATE 1987	EXPLANATION	POST. REF.	DEBIT	CREDIT	BALANCE

Cindy Carrel   ACCOUNT NO.

DATE 1987	EXPLANATION	POST. REF.	DEBIT	CREDIT	BALANCE

Charles Coleman   ACCOUNT NO.

DATE 1987	EXPLANATION	POST. REF.	DEBIT	CREDIT	BALANCE

John Grant   ACCOUNT NO.

DATE 1987	EXPLANATION	POST. REF.	DEBIT	CREDIT	BALANCE

James Hood   ACCOUNT NO.

DATE 1987	EXPLANATION	POST. REF.	DEBIT	CREDIT	BALANCE

(a) (c) (Continued)

V. P. Stone   ACCOUNT NO.

DATE 1987	EXPLANATION	POST. REF.	DEBIT	CREDIT	BALANCE

Janice Thompson   ACCOUNT NO.

DATE 1987	EXPLANATION	POST. REF.	DEBIT	CREDIT	BALANCE

Jim Westerling   ACCOUNT NO.

DATE 1987	EXPLANATION	POST. REF.	DEBIT	CREDIT	BALANCE

(a) (c) (Concluded)

SPORTSWEAR OUTLET STORE
SUBSIDIARY ACCOUNTS PAYABLE LEDGER

Athletic Shoe Corporation   ACCOUNT NO.

DATE 1987		EXPLANATION	POST. REF.	DEBIT	CREDIT	BALANCE

Rackets, Inc.   ACCOUNT NO.

DATE 1987		EXPLANATION	POST. REF.	DEBIT	CREDIT	BALANCE

Sports Clothes, Inc.   ACCOUNT NO.

DATE 1987		EXPLANATION	POST. REF.	DEBIT	CREDIT	BALANCE

Comprehensive Review Problem 6-1

Name _____

(b)

SPORTSWEAR OUTLET STORE
SALES JOURNAL

Page 6

DATE	CUSTOMER	INVOICE NUMBER	ACCOUNTS RECEIVABLE, DR. SALES, CR.	
			✓	AMOUNT

SPORTSWEAR OUTLET STORE
CASH RECEIPTS JOURNAL

Page 6

DATE	DESCRIPTION	SALES, CR.	ACCOUNTS RECEIVABLE, CR.		OTHER ACCOUNTS, CR.			SALES DISCOUNTS, DR.	CASH, DR.
			✓	AMOUNT	ACCOUNT TITLE	ACCT. NO.	✓	AMOUNT	

Comprehensive Review Problem 6-1

Name

(b) (Continued)

SPORTSWEAR OUTLET STORE
PURCHASES JOURNAL

Page 6

DATE	CREDITOR	TERMS	INVOICE NUMBER	PURCHASES, DR. ACCOUNTS PAYABLE, CR. AMOUNT	

SPORTSWEAR OUTLET STORE
CASH DISBURSEMENTS JOURNAL

Page 6

DATE	DESCRIPTION	CHECK NO.	CASH, CR.	PURCHASE DISCOUNTS, CR.

ACCOUNTS PAYABLE, DR. AMOUNT		ACCOUNT TITLE	OTHER ACCOUNTS, DR. ACCT. NO.	AMOUNT	

(b) (f)

**SPORTSWEAR OUTLET STORE
GENERAL JOURNAL**

DATE	ACCOUNT TITLES AND EXPLANATION	POST. REF.	DEBIT	CREDIT
	Adjusting Entries			

Working paper for Comprehensive Review Problem part (d) appears in back of manual

(e)

SPORTSWEAR OUTLET STORE

Income Statement

For the Month Ended December 31, 1987

Revenues:					
Gross sales					$
Less: Sales discounts			$		
Sales returns and allowances					
Net sales					$
Cost of goods sold:					
Merchandise inventory, Dec. 1, 1987				$	
Purchases		$			
Less: Purchase discounts	$				
Purchase returns and allowances					
Net purchases		$			
Add: Transportation-in					
Net cost of purchases					
Goods available for sale				$	
Merchandise inventory Dec. 31, 1987					
Cost of goods sold					
Gross margin					$
Operating expenses:					
Selling expenses:					
Rent		$			
Supplies					
Depreciation-store equipment				$	
Administrative expenses:					
Insurance		$			
Depreciation – office furniture					
Total operating expenses					
Net income from operations					$
Nonoperating revenue:					
Miscellaneous revenue					
Net Income					$

SPORTSWEAR OUTLET STORE
Balance Sheet
December 31, 1987

ASSETS							
Current assets:							
Cash							
Accounts receivable							
Prepaid insurance							
Supplies on hand							
Merchandise inventory							
Total current assets							
Property, plant, and equipment:							
Office furniture							
Less: Accumulated depreciation							
Store equipment							
Less: Accumulated depreciation							
Total property, plant, and equipment							
Total Assets							
LIABILITIES AND OWNER'S EQUITY							
Current liabilities:							
Accounts payable							
Owner's equity:							
Jack Springs, Capital							
Total Liabilities and Owner's Equity							

SPORTSWEAR OUTLET STORE
GENERAL JOURNAL

(f) (Concluded)   Page 7

DATE	ACCOUNT TITLES AND EXPLANATION	POST. REF.	DEBIT	CREDIT
	Closing Entries			

Comprehensive Review Problem 6-1

Name_____

(h)

SPORTSWEAR OUTLET STORE

Post-Closing Trial Balance

December 31, 1987

ACCT. NO.	ACCOUNT TITLE	DEBITS	CREDITS
1	Cash		
2	Accounts receivable		
3	Prepaid insurance		
4	Supplies on hand		
5	Merchandise inventory		
6	Office furniture		
7	Accumulated depreciation – office furniture		
8	Store equipment		
9	Accumulated depreciation – store equipment		
10	Accounts payable		
11	Jack Springs, capital		
(i)	**SPORTSWEAR OUTLET STORE**		
	Schedule of Accounts Receivable		
	As of December 31, 1987		
	Sallie Branscom		
	John Grant		
	James Hood		
	Janice Thompson		
	Jim Westerling		
	Balance in the control account		
	SPORTSWEAR OUTLET STORE		
	Schedule of Accounts Payable		
	As of December 31, 1987		
	Athletic Shoe Corporation		
	Sports Clothes, Inc.		
	Balance in the control account		

(a)   _____

Bank Reconciliation Statement

_____ ___ , 1987

Balance per bank statement, _____ ___ , 1987		
Balance per ledger, _____ ___ , 1987		

ENTRY

(b)

	DEBIT	CREDIT

_____ **COMPANY**
GENERAL JOURNAL

DATE	ACCOUNT TITLES AND EXPLANATION	POST. REF.	DEBIT	CREDIT
1987				

GENERAL JOURNAL

DATE	ACCOUNT TITLES AND EXPLANATION	POST. REF.	DEBIT	CREDIT

_____ **COMPANY**

Bank Reconciliation Statement

_____ ___ , 1987

			DEBIT	CREDIT
Balance per bank statement, _____ ___ , 1987				
Balance per ledger, _____ ___ , 1987				
ENTRY				

(a)   _____ **COMPANY**

Bank Reconciliation Statement

_____ ____ , 1987

		DEBIT	CREDIT
Balance per bank statement, _____ ____ , 1987 _____			
Balance per ledger, _____ ____ , 1987			

ENTRY

(b)

COMPANY

Voucher Register

DATE 19--	VCHR. NO.	PAYEE	EXPLANATION	TERMS	DATE PAID	CK. NO.	VCHRS. PAY., CR.	MDSE. PUR., DR.	TRANS- IN, DR.	DISC. LOST, DR.	OTHER ACCOUNT DEBIT ACCT. NAME	NO.	AMT.	✓
1														
2														
3														
4														
5														
6														
7														
8														
9														
10														
11														
12														
13														
14														
15														
16														
17														
18														
19														
20														
21														
22														
23														
24														
25														
26														
27														

_____ **COMPANY**
CHECK REGISTER

	DATE		PAYEE	VCHR. NO.	CHK. NO.	VOUCHERS PAYABLE DR. CASH CR.	
	1987						
1							
2							
3							
4							
5							
6							
7							
8							
9							
10							
11							
12							
13							
14							
15							
16							
17							
18							
19							
20							
21							
22							
23							
24							
25							
26							
27							
28							
29							
30							
31							
32							
33							
34							
35							
36							
37							
38							
39							
40							
41							
42							

Problem 7-7-A or 7-7-B

_____ COMPANY

Voucher Register

DATE 19--	VCHR. NO.	PAYEE	EXPLANATION	TERMS	DATE PAID	CK. NO.	VCHRS. PAY. CR.	MDSE. PUR. DR.	TRANS- IN DR.	DISC. LOST DR.	OTHER ACCOUNT DEBIT ACCT. NAME	NO.	AMT.	✓
1														
2														
3														
4														
5														
6														
7														
8														
9														
10														
11														
12														
13														
14														
15														
16														
17														
18														
19														
20														
21														
22														
23														
24														
25														
26														
27														

_____ **COMPANY**

CHECK REGISTER

	DATE		PAYEE	VCHR. NO.	CHK. NO.	VOUCHERS PAYABLE DR. CASH CR.	
	1987						
1							
2							
3							
4							
5							
6							
7							
8							
9							
10							
11							
12							
13							
14							
15							
16							
17							
18							
19							
20							
21							
22							
23							
24							
25							
26							
27							
28							
29							
30							
31							
32							
33							
34							
35							
36							
37							
38							
39							
40							
41							
42							

GENERAL LEDGER

Vouchers Payable   **ACCOUNT NO. 250**

DATE		EXPLANATION	POST. REF.	DEBIT	CREDIT	BALANCE

_____ **COMPANY** _____

List of Unpaid Vouchers

January 31, 1988

SAM BROWN

WARNER COMPANY

(a)

(b) Bank Reconciliation Statement, December 31, 1987

(c)

The following weaknesses currently exist: _____

_____

_____

_____

_____

_____

_____

_____

_____

_____

_____

_____

_____

_____

The following procedures would improve the internal control system: _____

_____

_____

_____

_____

_____

_____

_____

_____

_____

_____

_____

_____

_____

_____

_____

_____

_____

_____

_____

_____

_____

_____ **COMPANY**

GENERAL JOURNAL

DATE	ACCOUNT TITLES AND EXPLANATION	POST. REF.	DEBIT	CREDIT
(a)				
(b)				

Name _____

COMPANY

General Journal Entries

ACCOUNT TITLES	1986 Dr.	1986 Cr.	1987 Dr.	1987 Cr.	1988 Dr.	1988 Cr.
(a)						
(b)						
(c)						

GENERAL JOURNAL

DATE	ACCOUNT TITLES AND EXPLANATION	POST. REF.	DEBIT	CREDIT

(a)

(b)

(c)

(d)

(e)

(f)

(g)

Name_____

(a)

(b)

(c)

(d)

(e)

(f)

_____ **COMPANY**
GENERAL JOURNAL

DATE	ACCOUNT TITLES AND EXPLANATION	POST. REF.	DEBIT	CREDIT
(a)				
(b)				
(c)				

_____ **COMPANY**
GENERAL JOURNAL

DATE	ACCOUNT TITLES AND EXPLANATION	POST. REF.	DEBIT	CREDIT

GENERAL JOURNAL

DATE	ACCOUNT TITLES AND EXPLANATION	POST. REF.	DEBIT	CREDIT

THE _____ **COMPANY**
GENERAL JOURNAL

DATE	ACCOUNT TITLES AND EXPLANATION	POST. REF.	DEBIT	CREDIT

GENERAL JOURNAL

DATE	ACCOUNT TITLES AND EXPLANATION	POST. REF.	DEBIT	CREDIT

(a)

(b)

_____ COMPANY

Schedule of Corrected Income

	1987	1988	1989	TOTAL
Reported Income				
Errors Corrected:				
Inventory 12/31/87				
Understated				
Inventory 12/31/88				
Overstated				
Corrected Income				

(a)

_____ COMPANY

	1984	1985	1986	1987	TOTAL
Reported Income					
Corrections					
(2)					
(3)					
(4)					
(5)					
Corrected Income					

(b) Errors in balance sheets:

December 31, 1984:

December 31, 1985:

December 31, 1986:

December 31, 1987:

(c)

_____ COMPANY

(a)

(b)

(c)

_____ COMPANY

(a)

(b)

(c)

(d)

(a)   _____ COMPANY
                          Schedules of Alternative Inventory Valuations

(1)

(2)

(3)

_____ **COMPANY**

(b)

GENERAL JOURNAL

DATE	ACCOUNT TITLES AND EXPLANATION	POST. REF.	DEBIT	CREDIT

Name

OGLESBY   COMPANY

Schedules of Gross Margins

	1985	1986	1987
(a) FIFO:			
(b) LIFO:			

(a)   FAIRFIELD COMPANY

	UNITS	UNIT COST	TOTAL COST
Fifo:			
For 1987:			
For 1988:			

(b)

Lifo:	UNITS	UNIT COST	TOTAL COST
For 1987:			
For 1988:			

_____ COMPANY

_____ COMPANY

Schedule of Inventory Valuation

December 31, 1987

ITEM	COST	MARKET	LOWER, COST OR MARKET

(a)

(b)

(c)   (9-8-B only)

CHAPMAN COMPANY

(a)

(b)

Computation of Ending Inventory

HUDSON COMPANY

(a)

(b)

HUDSON COMPANY
Income Statements for the Quarters Ended March 31, 1987, and June 30, 1987
and for the Six Months Ended June 30, 1987

	First Quarter	Second Quarter	Six Months Ended 6-30-87

_____ COMPANY

	COST						RETAIL PRICE					
Beginning inventory													
Purchases													
Purchases returns													
Transportation-in													
Goods available for sale													
Sales													
Estimated ending inventory at retail													
Cost/retail price ratio:													
Inventory valued at cost:													

TALLY COMPANY

(a)

GENERAL JOURNAL

DATE	ACCOUNT TITLES AND EXPLANATION	POST. REF.	DEBIT	CREDIT
(b)				
(c)				

MONROE COMPANY
GENERAL JOURNAL

DATE	ACCOUNT TITLES AND EXPLANATION	POST. REF.	DEBIT	CREDIT

JACKSON COMPANY

ANNE FERRELL

_____ COMPANY

Schedule of Land Cost

Name_____

_____ COMPANY

Schedule of Machine Cost

Name_____

_____ COMPANY

AUSTIN COMPANY

Schedule of Truck Cost

(a)

(b)

(c)

CONE COMPANY
GENERAL JOURNAL

DATE	ACCOUNT TITLES AND EXPLANATION	POST. REF.	DEBIT	CREDIT
(a)				
(b)				
(c)				

(a)   **RAINBOW COMPANY**
                              Schedule of Costs Incurred

ITEM	LAND	LAND IMPROVEMENTS	BUILDINGS	MACHINERY

RAINBOW COMPANY
GENERAL JOURNAL

(b)

DATE	ACCOUNT TITLES AND EXPLANATION	POST. REF.	DEBIT	CREDIT

(a)
MEDLEY COMPANY
Schedule of Building Cost
December 31, 1987

MEDLEY COMPANY
GENERAL JOURNAL

(b)

DATE	ACCOUNT TITLES AND EXPLANATION	POST. REF.	DEBIT	CREDIT

CORBIN COMPANY
GENERAL JOURNAL

DATE	ACCOUNT TITLES AND EXPLANATION	POST. REF.	DEBIT	CREDIT
(a)	Depreciation Expense			
(b)	Depreciation Expense			
(c)	Depreciation Expense			
(d)	Depreciation Expense			

REDDING COMPANY

(a)   Straight-line depreciation:

(b)   Units-of-production depreciation:

(c)   Sum-of-the-years'-digits depreciation:

(d)   Double-declining-balance depreciation:

Name_____

_____ COMPANY

	Computations	Depreciation Expense for	
		1987	1988
(a)	Straight-line		
(b)	Sum-of-the-years'-digits		
(c)	Double-declining-balance		

ROLLAND COMPANY
Schedule to Compute Cost of Land, Buildings, and Land Improvements
December 31, 1987

		LAND	BUILDINGS	LAND IMPROVEMENTS	
(a)	DEBITS				
	CREDIT				
(b)					

(c)

ROLLAND COMPANY
GENERAL JOURNAL

DATE		ACCOUNT TITLES AND EXPLANATION	POST. REF.	DEBIT	CREDIT

(a)   MELTON COMPANY

(1)

(2)

(3)

(4)

(b)

_____ **COMPANY**

GENERAL JOURNAL

DATE	ACCOUNT TITLES AND EXPLANATION	POST. REF.	DEBIT	CREDIT

GENERAL JOURNAL

DATE	ACCOUNT TITLES AND EXPLANATION	POST. REF.	DEBIT	CREDIT
(a)				
(b)				

(a) _____ COMPANY

Schedule to Compute Book Value

_____ ____ , 1988

_____ **COMPANY**

GENERAL JOURNAL

DATE		ACCOUNT TITLES AND EXPLANATION	POST. REF.	DEBIT	CREDIT
(b)					
(c)					

_____ **COMPANY**

GENERAL JOURNAL

(c) (Concluded)

DATE	ACCOUNT TITLES AND EXPLANATION	POST. REF.	DEBIT	CREDIT

_____ **COMPANY**

GENERAL JOURNAL

DATE	ACCOUNT TITLES AND EXPLANATION	POST. REF.	DEBIT	CREDIT

_____ **COMPANY**
GENERAL JOURNAL

DATE	ACCOUNT TITLES AND EXPLANATION	POST. REF.	DEBIT	CREDIT

_____ **COMPANY**

GENERAL JOURNAL

DATE	ACCOUNT TITLES AND EXPLANATION	POST. REF.	DEBIT	CREDIT

CRADDOCK COMPANY
GENERAL JOURNAL

DATE	ACCOUNT TITLES AND EXPLANATION	POST. REF.	DEBIT	CREDIT

MANNING MINING COMPANY

(a)   Depletion for 1987:

(b)   Depreciation for 1987:
           Units-of-Production Basis

(c)

_____ **COMPANY**
GENERAL JOURNAL

DATE	ACCOUNT TITLES AND EXPLANATION	POST. REF.	DEBIT	CREDIT

_____ **COMPANY**

GENERAL JOURNAL

DATE	ACCOUNT TITLES AND EXPLANATION	POST. REF.	DEBIT	CREDIT
(a)				
(b)				
(c)				
(d)				
(e)				
(f)	(P11-8-B only)			

JOHNSTON COMPANY
GENERAL JOURNAL

DATE 1987	ACCOUNT TITLES AND EXPLANATION	POST. REF.	DEBIT	CREDIT
(a)				
(b)				

JOHNSTON COMPANY
GENERAL JOURNAL

DATE	ACCOUNT TITLES AND EXPLANATION	POST. REF.	DEBIT	CREDIT
(c)				

(d)

(e)

WILL RAWLEY
GENERAL JOURNAL

DATE	ACCOUNT TITLES AND EXPLANATION	POST. REF.	DEBIT	CREDIT
(a) (1)				
(2)				
(b)				

(a)

(b)

GENERAL JOURNAL

DATE	ACCOUNT TITLES AND EXPLANATION	POST. REF.	CREDIT	DEBIT

(a)

(b)

(c)

(d)

GENERAL JOURNAL

DATE		ACCOUNT TITLES AND EXPLANATION	POST. REF.	DEBIT	CREDIT

Problem 12-4-A or 12-4-B

Name _____

(a) and (b)

Payroll Journal

DATE WEEK ENDED	EMPLOYEE	OFFICE SALARIES EXPENSE	SALARIES EXPENSE	FEDERAL INCOME TAXES PAYABLE	F I C A TAXES PAYABLE	STATE INCOME TAXES PAYABLE	MEDICAL INSURANCE PREM. PAYABLE	SALARIES PAYABLE	CHECK NO.

GENERAL JOURNAL

DATE	ACCOUNT TITLES AND EXPLANATION	POST. REF.	DEBIT	CREDIT
(c)				
(d)				
(e)	(12-4-A only)			

(e) (12-4-B only)

Cash

Salaries Payable

Employees' Federal Income Taxes Payable

F.I.C.A. Taxes Payable

Employees' State Income Taxes Payable

Employees' Medical Insurance Payable

State Unemployment Taxes Payable

Federal Unemployment Taxes Payable

Cooks' Salaries Expense

Office Salaries Expense

Payroll Taxes Expense

Part I _____

(a) _____

GENERAL JOURNAL

DATE		ACCOUNT TITLES AND EXPLANATION	POST REF.	DEBIT	CREDIT
(b) 1987		If accrual not to include payroll taxes:			
Dec.	31				
1987		If accrual to include payroll taxes:			
Dec.	31				

GENERAL JOURNAL

DATE	ACCOUNT TITLES AND EXPLANATION	POST REF.	DEBIT	CREDIT
1987				
(a)				
(b)				

(a)

(b)

QUARTERMAINE COMPANY

(a)   Sales revenue

(b)   Realized gross margin:

Name_____

_____ COMPANY

(In thousands)

(a)	Revenues (completed contracts only)							
	Net Income							
(b)	Revenues:							
	Cost of revenues:							

(a) _____ COMPANY

Partial Statement of Current Cost Net Income

Sales

Cost of goods sold

Depreciation

Other expenses

Net income from continuing operations

(b) _____ COMPANY

Partial Statement of Constant Dollar Net Income

Sales

Cost of goods sold

Depreciation

Other expenses

Net income from continuing operations

_____ COMPANY

Restated Income for the Year Ended December 31, 1987

(in constant end-of-year 1987 dollars)

	Historical Dollars	Conversion Ratio	Constant Dollars

(a)

Partial Statement of Current Cost Net Income

For the Year Ended _____ _____, 19_____

Sales

Cost of goods sold

Depreciation expense

Other expenses

Net income from continuing operations

(b)

Partial Statement of Constant Dollar Net Income

In _____ _____, 19_____, Dollars

For the Year Ended _____ _____, 19_____

Sales

Cost of goods sold

Depreciation expense

Other expenses

Net income from continuing operations

OAKLAND CLEANING COMPANY
Restated Income for the year Ended December 31, 1987
(in constant end-of-year 1987 dollars)

	Historical Dollars	Conversion Ratio	Constant Dollars
(a)			
Service revenue			
Supplies expense			
Rent expense			
Depreciation expense			
Other expenses			
Total Expenses			
Net income from operations			
Purchasing power loss on net monetary items			
Net Income			

(b)

(c)

_____ **and** _____
GENERAL JOURNAL

DATE	ACCOUNT TITLES AND EXPLANATION	POST. REF.	DEBIT	CREDIT
1987				
	Cash			
	Accounts Receivable			
	Inventory			

(a) _____ and _____

Schedule of Distribution of Net Income
For the year Ended December 31, 1987

			TOTAL	AMOUNT TO BE DISTRIBUTED
Net income				
Salaries				
Interest				
Remainder				
Distribution				

GENERAL JOURNAL

DATE		ACCOUNT TITLES AND EXPLANATION	POST. REF.	DEBIT	CREDIT
1987					
Dec.	31	Income Summary			

(b) _____ and _____

Schedule of Distribution of Net Income
For the Year Ended December 31, 1987

			TOTAL	AMOUNT TO BE DISTRIBUTED
Net income				
Salaries				
Interest				
Remainder				
Distribution				

GENERAL JOURNAL

DATE		ACCOUNT TITLES AND EXPLANATION	POST. REF.	DEBIT	CREDIT
1987					
Dec.	31	Income Summary			

(a)

K AND M

Schedule of Distribution of Net Income

For the Year Ended June 30, 1988

(1)

	K	M	TOTAL	AMOUNT TO BE DISTRIBUTED
Net Income				
Salaries				
Remainder				
Distribution				

(2)

			TOTAL	AMOUNT TO BE DISTRIBUTED
Net Income				
Salaries				
Interest				
Remainder equally				
Distribution				

(a)

S AND C

Schedule of Distribution of Net Income

For the Year Ended December 31, 1987

	S	C	TOTAL	AMOUNT TO BE DISTRIBUTED
Net income				
Salaries				
Interest				
Remainder				
Distribution				

GENERAL JOURNAL

DATE	ACCOUNT TITLES AND EXPLANATION	POST. REF.	DEBIT	CREDIT
	Income Summary			

(b)

(b) 14-3-A
(c) 14-3-B
_____ and _____

Statement of Partner's Capital
For the Year Ended December 31, 1987

Balance, _____ _____, 1987

Net income for the year:

(c) (14-3-A only)

GENERAL JOURNAL

DATE	ACCOUNT TITLES AND EXPLANATION	POST. REF.	DEBIT	CREDIT

(a) ＿＿＿＿＿＿＿＿＿＿＿＿ and ＿＿＿＿＿＿＿＿＿

Schedule of Distribution of Net Income

For the Year Ended ＿＿＿＿ ＿＿＿, 19＿＿＿

			TOTAL	AMOUNT TO BE DISTRIBUTED
Net ＿＿＿＿＿＿＿＿＿				
Salaries				
Remainder				
Distribution				

			TOTAL	AMOUNT TO BE DISTRIBUTED
(b)				
Net ＿＿＿＿＿＿＿＿＿				
Salaries				
Interest				
Remainder				
Distribution				

_____ and _____
Schedule of Distribution of Net Income
For the _____

			TOTAL	AMOUNT TO BE DISTRIBUTED

and _____

(a)

GENERAL JOURNAL

DATE	ACCOUNT TITLES AND EXPLANATION	POST. REF.	DEBIT	CREDIT

(a) (Concluded)   _____ and _____

Schedule of Distribution of Net Income
For the Year Ended _____ _____, 1987

				TOTAL	AMOUNT TO BE DISTRIBUTED
Net income					
Salaries					
Interest:					
Remainder					
Distribution					

GENERAL JOURNAL

DATE	ACCOUNT TITLES AND EXPLANATION	POST. REF.	DEBIT	CREDIT

(b) _____ and _____

Income Statement

For the Year Ended _____ _____, 1987

Distribution of Net Income			
Salaries			
Interest			
Remainder			
Totals			

(c) _____ _____ and _____

Statement of Partners' Capital

For the Year Ended _____, 1987

	_____	_____	TOTAL

(d) _____ _____ and _____

Balance Sheet

_____ _____, 1987

Assets

Current Assets:

Liabilities and Owners' Equity

Current Liabilities:

GENERAL JOURNAL

DATE (or entry no.)	ACCOUNT TITLES AND EXPLANATION	POST. REF.	DEBIT	CREDIT
(a)				
(b)				
(c)				
(d)				
(e)	(14-7-A only)			

_____ and _____
GENERAL JOURNAL

DATE (or entry no.)		ACCOUNT TITLES AND EXPLANATION	POST. REF.	DEBIT	CREDIT
(a)					
(b)					
(c)					
(d)		(Prob 14-8-B only)			

_____ **and** _____
GENERAL JOURNAL

DATE (or entry no.)		ACCOUNT TITLES AND EXPLANATION	POST. REF.	DEBIT	CREDIT
(a)					
(b)					
(c)					

GENERAL JOURNAL

DATE (or entry no.)		ACCOUNT TITLES AND EXPLANATION	POST. REF.	DEBIT	CREDIT
(a)					
(b)					
(c)		(14-10-A only)			

GENERAL JOURNAL

DATE 1987		ACCOUNT TITLES AND EXPLANATION	POST. REF.	DEBIT	CREDIT
Jan.					

GENERAL JOURNAL

DATE	ACCOUNT TITLES AND EXPLANATION	POST. REF.	DEBIT	CREDIT

(a)
HULL AND DAVIS
Schedule of Proposed Distribution of Net Income
For the Year Ended December 31, 1987

	HULL	DAVIS	TOTAL	AMOUNT TO BE DISTRIBUTED
1987				
Net Income				
Salaries				
Interest				
Remainder equally				
Distribution				

(b)

(c)

(a)

(b)

	FIELDS	SIMS

Chapter 6
(Continued)

Comprehensive Review Problem 6-1

SPORTSWEAR OU

Work Sh

(d)

For the Month Ended De

ACCOUNT TITLES	TRIAL BALANCE		ADJUSTME
	DR.	CR.	DR.
Cash			
Accounts receivable			
Prepaid insurance			
Supplies on hand			
Merchandise inventory			
Office furniture			
Accumulated depreciation –			
office furniture			
Store equipment			
Accumulated depreciation –			
store equipment			
Accounts payable			
Jack Springs, capital			
Jack Springs, drawing			
Sales			
Sales discounts			
Sales returns and allowances			
Miscellaneous revenue			
Purchases			
Purchase discounts			
Purchase returns and allowances			
Transportation-in			
Rent expense			
Insurance expense			
Supplies expense			
Depreciation expense –			
office furniture			
Depreciation expense –			
store equipment			
Net income			

		ADJUSTED TRIAL BALANCE		INCOME STATEMENT		BALANCE SHEET	
CR.		DR.	CR.	DR.	CR.	DR.	CR.

CONNORS CABIN

Work Sh

For the Month Ende

ACCOUNT TITLES	TRIAL BALANCE		ADJUSTM
	DR.	CR.	DR.
Cash			
Merchandise Inventory			
Accounts Payable			
Ron Connors, Capital			
Sales			
Sales Discounts			
Sales Returns and Allowances			
Purchases			
Purchases Discounts			
Purchase Returns and Allowances			
Transportation-In			
Miscellaneous Selling Expenses			
Miscellaneous Administrative Expenses			
Net Income			

	CR.		ADJUSTED TRIAL BALANCE			INCOME STATEMENT			BALANCE SHEET	
			DR.	CR.		DR.	CR.		DR.	CR.

Work S
For the Year Ended D

ACCOUNT TITLES	TRIAL BALANCE		ADJUSTM
	DR.	CR.	DR.
Cash			
Accounts receivable			

Name _____

	ADJUSTED TRIAL BALANCE		INCOME STATEMENT		BALANCE SHEET	
CR.	DR.	CR.	DR.	CR.	DR.	CR.

MOORE DELIVERY S

Work S

For the Month End

(e)

ACCOUNT TITLES	TRIAL BALANCE		ADJUSTM
	DR.	CR.	DR.
Cash			
Accounts Receivable			
Supplies on Hand			
Prepaid Insurance			
Prepaid Rent			
Building			
Accumulated Depreciation — Building			
Trucks			
Accumulated Depreciation — Trucks			
Accounts Payable			
M. Moore, Capital			
M. Moore, Drawing			
Delivery Service Revenue			
Salaries Expense			
Utilities Expense			
Miscellaneous Expense			
Depreciation Expense — Building			
Depreciation Expense — Trucks			
Accrued Salaries Payable			
Supplies Expense			
Insurance Expense			
Rent Expense			

CE COMPANY _____

ne 30, 1987

	ADJUSTED TRIAL BALANCE		INCOME STATEMENT		BALANCE SHEET	
CR.	DR.	CR.	DR.	CR.	DR.	CR.

Work Sheet

For the Year Ended De

(a)

ACCOUNT TITLES	TRIAL BALANCE		ADJUSTM
	DR.	CR.	DR.

_____

r 31, 1987

		ADJUSTED TRIAL BALANCE		INCOME STATEMENT		BALANCE SHEET	
R.		DR.	CR.	DR.	CR.	DR.	CR.

(a)

Work S

For the Year Ended D

ACCOUNT TITLES	TRIAL BALANCE		ADJUSTM
	DR.	CR.	DR.

er 31, 1987

	ADJUSTED TRIAL BALANCE		INCOME STATEMENT		BALANCE SHEET	
R.	DR.	CR.	DR.	CR.	DR.	CR.

(a)

Work Shee

For the Year Ended Dec

ACCOUNT TITLES	TRIAL BALANCE		ADJUSTMEN
	DR.	CR.	DR.

Name

	ADJUSTED TRIAL BALANCE		INCOME STATEMENT		BALANCE SHEET	
CR.	DR.	CR.	DR.	CR.	DR.	CR.

ADJUSTED TRIAL BALANCE		INCOME STATEMENT		BALANCE SHEET	
DR.	CR.	DR.	CR.	DR.	CR.

ACCOUNT TITLES	TRIAL BALANCE		ADJUS
	DR.	CR.	DR.
Cash			
Accounts Receivable			
Merchandise Inventory			
Land			
Mike Hall, Capital			
Sales			
Sales Discounts			
Sales Returns and Allowances			
Purchases			
Purchase Discounts			
Purchase Returns and Allowances			
Transportation-In			
Rent Expense			
Office Salaries Expense			
Sales Salaries Expense			
Net Income			

Check Figures

Chapters 1-28

Chapter 1

P1-1-A	(b) Total assets, $140,000
P1-2-A	(b) Total assets, $225,000
P1-3-A	(b) Net income, $7,000
P1-4-A	(b) Total assets, $46,320
P1-5-A	(c) Total assets, $114,000
P1-6-A	(b) Net loss, $2,320
P1-7-A	(b) Net income, $80,000
P1-1-B	(b) Total assets, $185,000
P1-2-B	(b) Total assets, $140,000
P1-3-B	(b) Net income, $1,040
P1-4-B	(b) Total assets, $44,500
P1-5-B	(c) Total assets, $47,600
P1-6-B	(b) Net income, $11,620
P1-7-B	(b) Net income, $17,040
Bus. Dec. Prob. 1-1	
	No check figure
Bus. Dec. Prob. 1-2	
	(a) Net income, $25,200

Chapter 2

P2-1-A	No check figure
P2-2-A	No check figure
P2-3-A	Trial balance total, $103,070
P2-4-A	(b) Trial balance total, $122,925
P2-5-A	(b) Trial balance total, $178,000
P2-6-A	(d) Trial balance total, $269,960
P2-7-A	Trial balance total, $157,200
P2-1-B	No check figure
P2-2-B	No check figure
P2-3-B	Trial balance total, $47,880
P2-4-B	(b) Trial balance total, $39,180
P2-5-B	(b) Trial balance total, $29,700
P2-6-B	(d) Trial balance total, $772,380
P2-7-B	Trial balance total, $150,000
Bus. Dec. Prob.	
	(b) Cash account balance, $17,200

Chapter 3

P3-1-A	No check figure
P3-2-A	(b) Accumulated Depreciation — Machine account balance, $12,600
P3-3-A	Depreciation expense, $32,000
P3-4-A	(b) Prepaid Insurance account balance, $6,800
P3-5-A	Depreciation expense — equipment, $1,000
P3-6-A	Store Salaries Expense $810
P3-1-B	No check figure
P3-2-B	(b) Accumulated Depreciation — Truck, $15,000
P3-3-B	Depreciation Expense — Office Building, $17,600
P3-4-B	(b) Service Revenue account balance, $186,000
P3-5-B	Insurance expense, $1,200
P3-6-B	Depreciation expense — building, $4,000
Bus. Dec. Prob.	
	(b) Net income, $43,500

Chapter 4

P4-1-A	Net income, $25,600
P4-2-A	Net income, $28,540
P4-3-A	(b) Owner's capital balance after closing, $105,860
P4-4-A	Net loss, $14,760
P4-5-A	Net income, $48,646
P4-6-A	Net income, $70,800
P4-7-A	Net income, $5,100
P4-1-B	Net income, $171,700
P4-2-B	Net income, $38,830
P4-3-B	(b) Owner's capital balance after closing, $459,000
P4-4-B	Net loss, $15,300
P4-5-B	Net loss, $77,580
P4-6-B	Net income, $173,150
P4-7-B	Net income, $54,450
Bus. Dec. Prob. 4-1	
	Net income, $82,200
Bus. Dec. Prob. 4-2	
	Net income, $52,400
Comp. Rev. Prob. 4-1	
	Net income, $43,800

Chapter 5

P5-1-A	No check figure
P5-2-A	Net amount due, $27,302.80
P5-3-A	Net amount due, $10,187.10
P5-4-A	(c) Trial balance total, $112,340
P5-5-A	Net income, $75,640
P5-6-A	Net income, $5,455
P5-1-B	No check figure
P5-2-B	Net amount due, $5,188.41
P5-3-B	Net amount due, $4,689.30
P5-4-B	(c) Trial balance total, $288,600
P5-5-B	Net income, $36,726
P5-6-B	Net income, $41,356
Bus. Dec. Prob.	
	Net income, $17,175

Chapter 6

P6-1-A	(a) Sales journal total, $6,500
P6-2-A	(b) Accounts Receivable ending balance, $28,300
P6-3-A	(b) Accounts Payable ending balance, $8,775
P6-4-A	Trial balance total, $170,750
P6-5-A	(c) Trial balance total, $245,296
P6-1-B	(a) Sales journal total, $6,000
P6-2-B	(b) Accounts Receivable ending balance, $308,000
P6-3-B	(b) Accounts Payable ending balance, $180,000
P6-4-B	Trial balance total, $193,460
P6-5-B	(c) Trial balance total, $137,160
Bus. Dec. Prob. 6-1	
	No check figure
Bus. Dec. Prob. 6-2	
	No check figure
Bus. Dec. Prob. 6-3	
	No check figure
Comp. Rev. Prob. 6-1	
	Net income, $6,901.50

Chapter 7

P7-1-A	(a) Adjusted cash balance, $45,168
P7-2-A	Cash Short and Over, Apr. 3rd debit, $1.25
P7-3-A	Cash Short and Over, June 22nd debit, $.80
P7-4-A	Adjusted cash balance, $18,973
P7-5-A	Adjusted cash balance, $60,600
P7-6-A	Check register total, $16,039
P7-7-A	Check register total, $22,854
P7-1-B	(a) Adjusted cash balance, $10,220.30
P7-2-B	Cash Short and Over, Dec. 17th debit, $4
P7-3-B	Cash Short and Over, Apr. 19th debit, $.54
P7-4-B	Adjusted cash balance, $13,750.93
P7-5-B	Adjusted cash balance, $19,476
P7-6-B	Check register total, $25,982
P7-7-B	Check register total, $189,984
Bus. Dec. Prob. 7-1	
	No check figure
Bus. Dec. Prob. 7-2	
	No check figure
Bus. Dec. Prob. 7-3	
	(b) Adjusted cash balance, $11,501.90
Bus. Dec. Prob. 7-4	
	No check figure

Chapter 8

P8-1-A	(b) Bad Debts Expense, $7,710
P8-2-A	(b) Bad Debts Expense, 1986, $7,500
P8-3-A	No check figure
P8-4-A	(e) Cash proceeds, $120,120
P8-5-A	No check figure
P8-6-A	June 20th cash proceeds, $7,967.32
P8-7-A	July 18th cash proceeds, $11,955.03
P8-1-B	(b) Bad Debts Expense, $6,620
P8-2-B	(b) 1986 Bad Debts Expense debit, $1,375
P8-3-B	No check figure
P8-4-B	(d) Cash proceeds, $55,738.80
P8-5-B	Nov. 16th cash proceeds, $29,400
P8-6-B	Nov. 20th cash proceeds, $3,983.66
P8-7-B	Sept. 5th cash proceeds, $62,055
Bus. Dec. Prob. 8-1	
	(a) Total benefit, $41,900
Bus. Dec. Prob. 8-2	
	No check figure

Chapter 9

P9-1-A	Correct net income 1988, $127,000
P9-2-A	(a) Corrected income 1986, $268,500
P9-3-A	(a) Gross margin, $32,200
P9-4-A	(a) Gross margin, $126,000
P9-5-A	(a) Fifo inventory, $4,730

©Business Publications, Inc., 1980, 1983, and 1986
1 2 3 4 5 6 7 8 9 0 CG 3 2 1 0 9 8 7 6
56-1345-03

P9-6-A	(a) 1987 Cost of goods sold under Fifo, $14,640
P9-7-A	1986 Net income under Lifo, $405,600
P9-8-A	(b) Lower-of-cost-or-market on item-by-item basis, $59,080
P9-9-A	(b) Estimated ending inventory, $167,246.40
P9-10-A	Ending inventory at cost, $210,000
P9-11-A	(a) Cost of goods sold, $370.05
P9-1-B	Correct net income 1988, $460,000
P9-2-B	(a) Corrected income 1986, $222,750
P9-3-B	(a) Gross margin, $26,300
P9-4-B	(a) Gross margin, $312,000
P9-5-B	(a) Fifo inventory, $22,800
P9-6-B	(a) 1987 Cost of goods sold, $108,375
P9-7-B	1987 Net income under Lifo, $688,000
P9-8-B	(b) Lower-of-cost-or-market on item-by-item basis, $37,020
P9-9-B	First quarter net income (before taxes), $46,000
P9-10-B	Ending inventory at cost, $79,800
P9-11-B	No check figure
Bus. Dec. Prob. 9-1	Cost of goods sold under Lifo, $47,730
Bus. Dec. Prob. 9-2	Estimated inventory, $52,800

Chapter 10

P10-1-A	Cost of land, $46,850
P10-2-A	Cost of machine, $46,040
P10-3-A	Cost of land, $429,450
P10-4-A	(b) Depreciation Expense, $6,030
P10-5-A	Total cost of buildings, $95,250
P10-6-A	(c) Sum-of-the-years'-digits' depreciation, $8,889
P10-7-A	(b) 1988 depreciation, $1,682
P10-1-B	Cost of land, $148,000
P10-2-B	Cost of machine, $7,740
P10-3-B	Cost of land, $174,860
P10-4-B	(b) Depreciation Expense, $11,000
P10-5-B	(a) Total cost of building, $317,600
P10-6-B	(a) Annual depreciation, $42,666.67
P10-7-B	(b) 1988 depreciation, $3,014
Bus. Dec. Prob. 10-1	Cost of land, $964,500
Bus. Dec. Prob. 10-2	(a) Units of production depreciation, $6,000

Chapter 11

P11-1-A	Loss on Disposal of Plant Assets, $1,425
P11-2-A	(b) Loss on Disposal of Plant Assets, $1,600
P11-3-A	(a) Book value of truck, $6,750
P11-4-A	Total Accumulated depreciation on old computers, $17,600
P11-5-A	Oct. 1 Debit to Trucks, $44,450
P11-6-A	Depreciation expense on building, $30,000
P11-7-A	Patent amortization expense for 1988, $24,000
P11-8-A	(c) Rent Expense, $4,000
P11-1-B	Loss on Disposal of Plant Assets, $1,760
P11-2-B	(b) Debit to Autos, $17,700
P11-3-B	(a) Book value of truck, $28,500
P11-4-B	Debit to Moving Vans, $49,000

P11-5-B	Loss on disposal of Truck B, $1,235
P11-6-B	(c) Average cost per ton, $4.35
P11-7-B	Patent amortization expense for 1988, $23,680
P11-8-B	(b) Patent amortization expense, $4,000
Bus. Dec. Prob. 11-1	(b) Loss on Trade-in of Machine A, $30,000
Bus. Dec. Prob. 11-2	(a)(2) Goodwill, $1,200,000

Chapter 12

P12-1-A	(b) Accrued payroll payable, $1,192.41
P12-2-A	(a) FICA tax for each, $44,161
P12-3-A	Accrued Payroll Payable, $40,230
P12-4-A	Total salaries payable, $2,447
P12-5-A	(l)(b) Payroll taxes expense, $2,639
P12-1-B	(b) Accrued payroll payable, $1,175.64
P12-2-B	(a) FICA tax for each, $47,940
P12-3-B	(a) Accrued Salaries Payable, $76,173
P12-4-B	Total Salaries payable, $1,746.60
P12-5-B	(l)(b) Payroll taxes expense, $1,015
Bus. Dec. Prob. 12-1	No check figure
Bus. Dec. Prob. 12-2	Additional cost to fill order under Alternative #2, $83,864

Chapter 13

P13-1-A	(b) Net income, $88,000
P13-2-A	(b) Net income, $11,800
P13-3-A	No check figure
P13-4-A	(b) Constant dollar net income, $12,000
P13-5-A	Constant dollar net loss, $2,500
P13-6-A	(b) Net income from continuing operations, $182,240
P13-1-B	(b) Net loss, $6,000
P13-2-B	(b) Net income, $950
P13-3-B	No check figure
P13-4-B	(a) Current cost net income, $23,800
P13-5-B	Constant dollar net income, $8,000
P13-6-B	(b) Net income from continuing operations, $22,000
Bus. Dec. Prob.	(a) Constant dollar net income, $2,605

Chapter 14

P14-1-A	Credit Jeff Poole, capital, $62,000
P14-2-A	(a) Distribution to Ladd, $23,400
P14-3-A	(a) Distribution to K, $176,000
P14-4-A	(a) Distribution to Chip, $106,950
P14-5-A	1987 Distribution to Kurt, $18,000
P14-6-A	(a) Distribution to Black, $5,692.50
P14-7-A	(d) Credit to Kelly, Capital, $126,000
P14-8-A	(b) Credit T, Capital, $43,500
P14-9-A	(b) Debit Beth Howe, Capital, $4,000
P14-10-A	(a) Debit T, Capital, $73,500
P14-11-A	Final debit to B, Capital, $60,000
P14-12-A	Final debit to Neal, Capital, $11,250
P14-1-B	Credit Karen Fisher, Capital, $44,000
P14-2-B	(a) Distribution to Clark, $34,800

P14-3-B	(a) Distribution to S, $50,400
P14-4-B	(a) Distribution to T, $(60,000)
P14-5-B	(a) Distribution to David, $57,000
P14-6-B	(a) Distribution to Bass, $32,045
P14-7-B	(d) Credit to Lee, Capital, $56,000
P14-8-B	(b) Credit R, Capital, $51,000
P14-9-B	(b) Debit Helen Burns, Capital, $6,000
P14-10-B	(b) Debit Gene, Capital, $7,250
P14-11-B	Final debit to Frank, Capital, $9,900
P14-12-B	Final debit to H, Capital, $8,800
Bus. Dec. Prob. 14-1	(a) Distribution to Hull, $79,000
Bus. Dec. Prob. 14-2	(b) Cash distribution to Fields, $127,500

Chapter 15

P15-1-A	Total paid-in capital, $388,800.
P15-2-A	1986 Preferred dividends, (a) $5,000, (b) $4,000.
P15-3-A	(b) Total stockholders' equity, $1,239,000.
P15-4-A	Paid-in capital in excess of par (stated) value, (a) $138,000, (b) $60,000; (c) Zero.
P15-5-A	(a) Paid-in capital in excess of par value, $9,000.
P15-6-A	(b) Total stockholders' equity, $2,044,000.
P15-7-A	(b) Total book value of common, $615,000.
P15-8-A	(3) Book value per share of preferred, $181.50.
P15-9-A	(c) Total cash payment, $636,000.
P15-1-B	Total paid-in capital, $851,000.
P15-2-B	1986 Preferred dividends, (a) $40,800; (b) $30,000.
P15-3-B	(b) Total stockholders' equity, $730,000.
P15-4-B	Paid-in capital in excess of par (stated) value, (a) $47,800, (b) $296,800; (c) Zero.
P15-5-B	(b) Total stockholders' equity, $27,000.
P15-6-B	(b) Total paid-in capital, $2,762,000.
P15-7-B	(b) Book value per share of common, $45.50.
P15-8-B	(c) Book value per share of preferred stock, $118.
P15-9-B	(c) Total cash payment, $50,250.
Bus. Dec. Prob. 15-1:	Dividends per share of preferred stock, Western Company, $2.00.
Bus. Dec. Prob. 15-2:	Book value per share of common stock, Simmons Corporation, $22.60.

Chapter 16

P16-1-A	Total stockholders' equity, $2,027,500.
P16-2-A	Dec. 1st, Paid-in capital – stock dividend, $1,200.
P16-3-A	No check figure.
P16-4-A	Appropriated retained earnings, Oct. 31st, $221,200.
P16-5-A	Aug. 4th, Paid-in capital — stock dividend, $80,000.
P16-6-A	Appropriated retained earnings, Dec. 31st, $280,000.
P16-7-A	(b) Total stockholders' equity, $290,400.
P16-8-A	(b) Total retained earnings, Dec. 31, 1987, $90,632.
P16-9-A	Net loss, $64,800.

P16-1-B	Total stockholders' equity, $928,200.
P16-2-B	Nov. 16, Paid-in capital — stock dividend, $24,000.
P16-3-B	Total stockholders' equity, $2,290,000.
P16-4-B	No check figure.
P16-5-B	No check figure.
P16-6-B	Total retained earnings, December 31, 1987, $1,182,000.
P16-7-B	(b) Total stockholders' equity, $2,242,750.
P16-8-B	(b) Total retained earnings, Oct. 31, 1987, $30,775.
P16-9-B	(a) Net income, $96,000.
Bus. Dec. Prob. 16-1	No check figure.
Bus. Dec. Prob. 16-2	No check figure.

Chapter 17

P17-1-A	(b) First period's interest expense, $12,743.
P17-2-A	Mar. 31: Dr. to Interest Expense of $4,396 for bond interest.
P17-3-A	(a) Mar. 31, 1988: Dr. to Bond Interest Expense, $13,500.
P17-4-A	(b) Carrying value of bonds payable on 6/30/88 is $64,846.
P17-5-A	(a) Price paid, $26,018.
P17-6-A	(a) Price received, $254,861.
P17-7-A	(a) Cost of bond investments, $50,972.
P17-8-A	(b) Long-term liabilities on Dec. 31, 1992, include $80,000 of bonds.
P17-1-B	(b) First period's interest, $10,348.
P17-2-B	Mar. 31, 1988: Dr. to Bond Interest Expense, $4,264.
P17-3-B	(a) Mar. 31, 1988: Dr. to Bond Interest Expense, $18,000.
P17-4-B	(b) Carrying value of the bonds on 9/30/88, $75,268.
P17-5-B	(a) Price paid, $30,092.
P17-6-B	(b) Carrying value of the bonds on 3/31/88, $223,658.
P17-7-B	(a) Cost of bond investments, $67,155.
P17-8-B	Long-term liabilities on Dec. 31, 1992, include $168,000 of bonds.
Bus. Dec. Prob. 17-1	EPS under alternative (2) are $2.72.
Bus. Dec. Prob. 17-2	R bonds have a present value of $1,195.

Chapter 18

P18-1-A	(c) Unrealized loss, $1,500.
P18-2-A	(c) Dec. 31, 1986: Net unrealized loss, $312.
P18-3-A	Credit to minority interest, $70,000.
P18-4-A	(b) Investment account balance, $1,502,018.
P18-5-A	Consolidated assets, $621,600.
P18-6-A	(a) Eliminations columns total to $375,000.
P18-7-A	Eliminations columns total to $406,313.
P18-8-A	(b) Consolidated retained earnings, $249,491.
P18-1-B	(b) Investments, $11,040.
P18-2-B	(a) Dec. 31, 1987: Recovery of market value, $3,360.
P18-3-B	(b) Credit to Minority intrest, $84,000.
P18-4-B	(b) Investment account balance, $496,090.
P18-5-B	Consolidated assets, $243,200.
P18-6-B	(a) Eliminations columns total to $462,000.
P18-7-B	Eliminations columns total to $501,000.
P18-8-B	(b) Consolidated retained earnings, $307,500. Problem: (b) Total assets, $870,000.

Chapter 19

P19-1-A	Total financial resources provided, $270,000.
P19-2-A	Cash provided by operations, $314,000.
P19-3-A	(b) Total financial resources provided, $248,400.
P19-4-A	(a) Total of columns in lower section of working paper, $256,800.
P19-5-A	(b) Total financial resources provided, $1,363,600.
P19-6-A	(a) Total of columns in lower section of working paper, $1,446,200.
P19-1-B	Total financial resources provided, $396,000.
P19-2-B	Cash provided by operations, $66,000.
P19-3-B	Total financial resources provided, $406,000.
P19-4-B	(a) Total of columns in lower section of working paper, $504,000.
P19-5-B	(b) Total financial resources provided, $378,000.
P19-6-B	(a) Total of columns in lower section of working paper, $416,000.
Bus. Dec. Prob. 19-1:	Cash provided by operations, $111,600.
Bus. Dec. Prob. 19-2:	Decrease in cash, $38,000.

Chapter 20

P20-1-A	Increase in net income, 22.7%.
P20-2-A	(a) Index for sales for 1989 is 133.
P20-3-A	(b) Current ratio, 1988, 2.71:1
P20-4-A	No check figure.
P20-5-A	(f) Dec. 31, 1988, equity ratio, 73.68%.
P20-6-A	(a) Co. 2 Turnover, 2.22 times
P20-7-A	(d) 1988 Times interest earned, $5.00.
P20-8-A	(a) Current ratio, 4.46:1
P20-9-A	(a) Inventory turnover, 1.56.
P20-1-B	Increase in net income, 114.3%.
P20-2-B	(a) 1989 sales index is 130.
P20-3-B	(b) Current ratio, 1988, 2.88:1
P20-4-B	No check figure.
P20-5-B	(b) 1988 total current liabilities = 28.02% of total liabilities and stockholders' equity.
P20-6-B	(a) Operating margin = 12.5%.
P20-7-B	(d) 1988 Times interest earned, 12.22.
P20-8-B	(a) Current ratio, 2.94:1.
P20-9-B	(a) Inventory turnover, 1.34.
Bus. Dec. Prob. 20-1	(a) Net income, $132,000.
Bus. Dec. Prob. 20-2	Credit sales for 82.95 days are outstanding at end of 1988.
Bus. Dec. Prob. 20-3	(a) (2) Using first advisor's estimates EPS are $0.38; ($0.05); $0.15.

Chapter 21

P21-1-A	(a) Cost of goods manufactured, $451,500.
P21-2-A	(a) Cost of goods manufactured, $342,100.
P21-3-A	Dr. Income Summary for $150,400 to close account in last entry.
P21-4-A	(a) Cost of goods manufactured, $696,900.
P21-5-A	(b) Cost of goods manufactured, $473,872.
P21-6-A	(c) Cost of goods sold, $1,480,800.
P21-7-A	Ending work in process inventory, $33,040.
P21-8-A	(b) Ending work in process inventory, $111,580.
P21-9-A	(b) Net income, $42,147.
P21-1-B	(a) Cost of goods manufactured, $600,000.
P21-2-B	(a) Cost of goods manufactured, $242,500.
P21-3-B	Dr. Income Summary for $82,250 to close the account.
P21-4-B	(a) Cost of goods manufactured, $387,000.
P21-5-B	(b) Cost of goods manufactured, $396,487.
P21-6-B	(b) Ending work in process inventory, $141,900.
P21-7-B	Ending work in process inventory, $27,000.
P21-8-B	No check figure.
P21-9-B	(c) Net income, $25,800.
Bus. Dec. Prob.	No check figure.

Chapter 22

P22-1-A	(b) Total overhead cost, $7,383.75.
P22-2-A	(b) Overhead applied, $1,520.
P22-3-A	(b) Overapplied overhead, $21,300.
P22-4-A	(d) Ending work in process inventory, $66,000.
P22-5-A	Work in process inventory, $98,250.
P22-6-A	(c) Ending work in process inventory, $130,000.
P22-7-A	Total unit cost, $4.66.
P22-8-A	(a) Total unit cost, $2.60.
P22-1-B	(b) Total overhead cost, $4,730.40.
P22-2-B	(a) Underapplied overhead when based on machine hours, $8,500.
P22-3-B	(d) Work in process inventory, July 31, 1987, $15,600.
P22-4-B	(b) Work in process inventory, $309,000.
P22-5-B	(c) Cost per equivalent unit, $4.77.
P22-6-B	Total cost per unit, $0.30.
P22-7-B	Total cost per unit, $1.05.
P22-8-B	Total unit cost, $0.93.
Bus. Dec. Prob.	(c) Unit cost per gallon in every quarter, $6.33.

Chapter 23

P23-1-A	Materials price variance, $330 unfavorable.
P23-2-A	Materials price variance, $234 favorable.
P23-3-A	Labor rate variance, $80,000 favorable.
P23-4-A	(b) Cost of Goods Sold debit, $41,250.
P23-5-A	(b) Overhead volume variance, $3,750 favorable.
P23-6-A	Overhead budget variance, $15,750 unfavorable.